ALEA JACTA EST !

GOSCINNY AND UDERZO
PRESENT
AN ASTERIX GAME BOOK

THE IDOL
OF THE GAULS

TRANSLATED BY DEREK HOCKRIDGE

HODDER AND STOUGHTON
LONDON   SYDNEY   AUCKLAND   TORONTO

British Library Cataloguing in Publication Data

Uderzo
The idol of the Gauls.
I. Title   II. Goscinny, *1926-1977*   III. Series
IV. La vedette Armoricaine. English
741.5944

ISBN 0-340-51422-1

Original edition © Editions Albert René, Goscinny-Uderzo, 1988
English translation © Editions Albert René, Goscinny-Uderzo, 1990
Exclusive licensee: Hodder and Stoughton Ltd
Translator: Derek Hockridge

First published in Great Britain 1990

Published by Hodder and Stoughton Children's Books,
a division of Hodder and Stoughton Ltd,
Mill Road, Dunton Green, Sevenoaks, Kent TN13 2YA

Typeset by SX Composing, Rayleigh, Essex

Printed in Belgium by Proost International Book Production

ADVENTURE SLAB

PERSONAL QUALITIES

FIGHTING FITNESS ☐ SKILL ☐ CHARM ☐

SECONDARY APTITUDE

OBJECTS (MAXIMUM 5)

FIGHTS

ENEMY	YOU	ENEMY	YOU	ENEMY	YOU	ENEMY	YOU	ENEMY	YOU

TESTS

DIFFICULTY	DIFFICULTY	DIFFICULTY

ENEMY	YOU	ENEMY	YOU	ENEMY	YOU	ENEMY	YOU	ENEMY	YOU

DIFFICULTY	DIFFICULTY	DIFFICULTY

MAGIC POTION

NUMBER OF DOSES

PURSE

NUMBER OF SESTERTII

NOTES

ADVENTURE SLAB

PERSONAL QUALITIES

FIGHTING FITNESS ☐   SKILL ☐   CHARM ☐

SECONDARY APTITUDE

OBJECTS (MAXIMUM 5)

FIGHTS

ENEMY	YOU	ENEMY	YOU	ENEMY	YOU	ENEMY	YOU	ENEMY	YOU

ENEMY	YOU	ENEMY	YOU	ENEMY	YOU	ENEMY	YOU	ENEMY	YOU

TESTS

DIFFICULTY	DIFFICULTY	DIFFICULTY

DIFFICULTY	DIFFICULTY	DIFFICULTY

MAGIC POTION
NUMBER OF DOSES

PURSE
NUMBER OF SESTERTII

NOTES

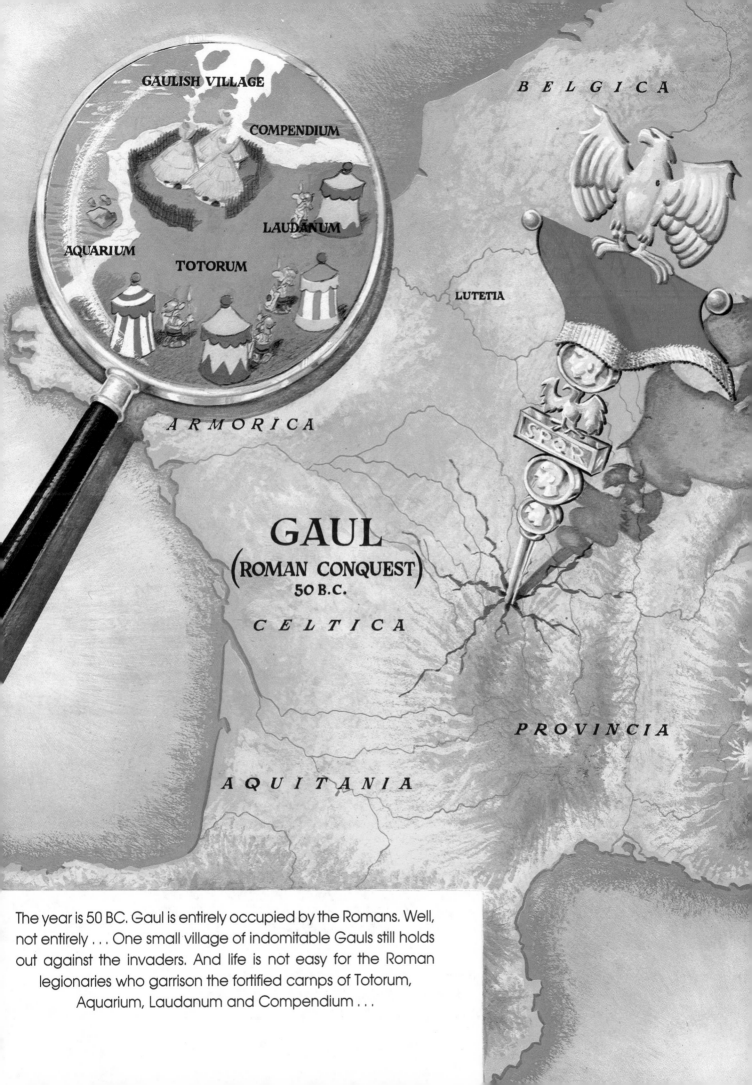

GAULISH VILLAGE

COMPENDIUM

LAUDANUM

AQUARIUM

TOTORUM

ARMORICA

BELGICA

LUTETIA

SPQR

GAUL
(ROMAN CONQUEST)
50 B.C.

CELTICA

PROVINCIA

AQUITANIA

The year is 50 BC. Gaul is entirely occupied by the Romans. Well, not entirely . . . One small village of indomitable Gauls still holds out against the invaders. And life is not easy for the Roman legionaries who garrison the fortified camps of Totorum, Aquarium, Laudanum and Compendium . . .

ALEA JACTA EST !

HERE IS A NEW KIND OF ASTERIX BOOK...

YOU ARE JUSTFORKIX, THE HERO OF THIS STORY.
YES, YOU YOURSELF ARE JUSTFORKIX, A YOUNG MAN
FROM LUTETIA. WE KNOW SOMETHING ABOUT YOU
ALREADY, FROM 'ASTERIX AND THE NORMANS'. IN
THAT BOOK, YOUR FATHER SENT YOU TO THE LITTLE
GAULISH VILLAGE TO TOUGHEN YOU UP A BIT. MAYBE
YOU DON'T HAVE QUITE THE STRENGTH OF OBELIX,
OR THE WISDOM OF GETAFIX, OR EVEN THE
EXPERIENCE OF ASTERIX, BUT NOBODY'S
PERFECT...

AND YOU ARE NOW ABOUT TO FACE DREADFUL
DANGERS. FROM PARAGRAPH TO PARAGRAPH, FROM
PERIL TO PERIL, YOU WILL HAVE TO MAKE DIFFICULT
DECISIONS, TAKE RISKY ACTION, THROW THE DICE
AND SEE WHAT LUCK CHANCE BRINGS YOU, GET
YOURSELF OUT OF COMPLICATED SITUATIONS, SOLVE
KNOTTY PROBLEMS. YOU WON'T ALWAYS BE
SUCCESSFUL... AND IF YOU AREN'T, YOU WILL
HAVE TO BEGIN THE ADVENTURE AGAIN.

BUT NEVER DESPAIR!
REMEMBER THAT YOU ARE AN
INDOMITABLE GAUL...

YOU WERE BORN IN LUTETIA NOT SO VERY LONG AGO...
YOUR PARENTS WERE SURE YOU WERE DESTINED
FOR GREAT THINGS...

SON, YOU WILL BE A SENATOR, AN EXPLORER, A GENERAL, A BARD...

...STRONG, SKILFUL, HANDSOME...

TODAY, ALL YOUR PARENTS' HOPES HAVE COME TRUE.
ALL OF THEM?

NO. TO BE HONEST, YOUR COURAGE AND STRENGTH OF
CHARACTER HAVE HARDLY BEEN PUT TO THE TEST...

SCREEEECH!

BUT NEVER MIND THAT! YOUR FATHER SENT
YOU TO SEE UNCLE VITALSTATISTIX, WHO LIVES
IN A LITTLE VILLAGE WE ALL KNOW WELL...

A VILLAGE WHERE TRUE GAULS
INTRODUCED YOU TO A MAN'S LIFE...

...TAUGHT YOU HOW
TO FIGHT...

LET 'EM COME! LET 'EM ALL COME!

...IN EVERY KIND
OF WAY...

BOO!

...AND HELPED YOU TO TAKE
DIFFICULT DECISIONS.

CHATTER-CHATTER!

YOU HAVE FOUND THAT CERTAIN
CIRCUMSTANCES LEND YOU WINGS...

...AND SOME-
TIMES EVEN
COURAGE!

BOING!
BOING!
BOING!

AND NOW, AT LAST, YOU
ARE READY FOR YOUR
GREAT ADVENTURE.
ALEA JACTA EST!

RULES OF THE GAME

You are going to have a thrilling and dangerous adventure in this book; you can be sure of that! But you may not be quite so sure how to play it yet.

So read the following rules carefully. They apply to all the ASTERIX game books in this series. They are clear and simple – don't hesitate to turn to them during the game if necessary.

CHANCE BOARD

All you need to play the game is this book, a pencil, and an eraser so that you can rub pencil marks out and play the game again. If you happen to have a dice, that's fine. But don't worry if you haven't. You can use the Chance Board which you will find at the end of the book.

ADVENTURE SLAB

You take the Adventure Slab with you on your adventures. It will come in useful when you want to note something down as a reminder, leaving you free to put your mind to other problems. You can detach it from the rest of the book, and then you get two for the price of one.

PERSONAL QUALITIES

Take a look at your Adventure Slab. You start out with three personal qualities.
- *Skill.*
- *Fighting Fitness.*
- *Charm.*

Each quality carries a number of points. It's up to you to decide on your own personality knowing that:
– you already have 10 points for each quality,
– you have an extra 15 points to divide between your qualities at the beginning of the adventure.

Record your choice on the Adventure Slab. Adding up the number of points your three qualities carry, you should get 45. If you don't get 45, either you've made a mistake or you've been cheating already!

SECONDARY APTITUDES

Needless to say, you weren't born yesterday, and you've already knocked about Gaul a bit. So you've learned some useful little tricks to use from day to day. At the beginning of the adventure, and sometimes in the middle of it, you will be told to choose between various aptitudes. Select whichever seems to you most useful, and remember to write it down on your Adventure Slab.

OBJECTS

A good legionary never goes anywhere without equipment. You can choose various objects which may turn out useful during your adventure, though on the other hand they may be more of a nuisance than anything else. And you can take only 5 objects. If you come across some other object during your travels and you want to take it with you, but you already have 5, you must get rid of one of them. You will find out what objects you can take in one of the early chapters.

NB: the gourd of magic potion and the purse of sestertii do not count as objects. They are extra items of equipment.

FIGHTS

Knowing you, you're bound to find yourself in situations where a punch-up or a spot of sword-play is called for.

To find out the result of your fights, follow these rules:

1. Enter your Fighting Fitness points in one of the Fights spaces on your Adventure Slab, plus any points that certain objects earn you – for instance, a sword or a shield.

2. Now write down your enemy's points. (You will find these given in the text.)

3. Throw the dice, or use the Chance Board, and subtract the number you get from your enemy's points score.

4. Throw the dice again, and subtract the number you get from your own score.

5. Carry on in the same way until your score or your enemy's score reaches 0. The loser is whichever of you reaches 0 first.

6. Unless there is any instruction telling you otherwise, you start again with the same original number of points next time you fight.

Example: a centurion takes you by surprise and challenges you to a duel. Suppose your score for Fighting Fitness is 15 and the centurion's score is 12. If you also have a sword (+5) and a shield (+3), your actual score for Fighting Fitness is thus 15+5+3 = 23.

Well done! You have won this particular fight . . . but it might not always be so easy.

NB: your Skill or Charm may also be used in a fight, depending on circumstances. When the time to use them comes, of course, you will be told.

FIGHTS AGAINST MORE THAN ONE ENEMY

In fights of this kind, you will be told either your enemies' total Fighting Fitness, and you have only one fight, or their individual Fighting Fitness, and you have more than one fight on your hands. But a word of warning . . . when fighting two enemies separately, and only then, you do not get your original Fighting Fitness score back to fight the second; you start with whatever points you have left from the first of the two fights.

TESTS

In certain other circumstances you may not have to fight an enemy, but you still have to pass a test of Skill, Fighting Fitness or Charm, using those qualities to get yourself out of a tricky situation. When that happens, follow these rules:

1. Always write down your points score for whichever quality is concerned, plus any extra points certain objects give you.

2. The degree of difficulty will always be given for each test, for instance: *difficulty 4*.

3. Now throw the dice as many times as the degree of difficulty indicates, for instance: *difficulty 4* = 4 throws of the dice, *difficulty 5* = 5 throws.

4. Each time you throw the dice, subtract the number you get from your own points score.

5. If you are left with a number above 0, you have succeeded. If you get 0 or a minus number, you have failed.

6. Unless you are told otherwise, you start again with your original points score when the next test comes up.

Example: you have to pass a test of skill with a difficulty factor of 4. You start with 14 points for Skill. You throw the dice 4 times and subtract the number from 14; for instance, 14−3−5−1−3 = 2. As the result is above 0, you have succeeded.

MAGIC POTION

If you drink some of Getafix's magic potion, you automatically win a fight or succeed in a test of your Fighting Fitness without needing to follow the usual rules. When the fight or the test is over, you lose your superhuman strength. You will then have to face the next fight or test in the usual way, unless you drink another dose of magic potion. Your gourd holds five doses at the beginning of your adventure.

Remember that:
– The magic potion will not work in fights or tests which call for you to use your personal qualities of Skill or Charm.

– You can drink magic potion only at the beginning of a fight or a test, never in the middle of it.
Keep a record of the number of doses of potion left in your gourd on your Adventure Slab.

PURSE

You are sure to need money on your travels. You must keep careful note of the number of sestertii you spend on your Adventure Slab.

THE END OF THE ADVENTURE

Sometimes, when you have lost a fight or made an error of judgment, you will read the fateful words: 'YOUR ADVENTURE IS OVER'.
Then you must start again at Chapter I.

CHAPTER I

YOU FALL ON YOUR FEET

Things happened so quickly that your head is still swimming. A Norseman has you by the shoulder and, turning towards you, bellows something that you don't understand . . . because of his accent!

'Get å møve øn! We're in a hurry!'

He thumps you on the back with his huge ham of a hand and you nearly fall over. Gradually, your brain begins to work again. Night had just fallen. You were making your way peacefully towards the village after a long walk when suddenly three Norsemen jumped out from behind a bush . . .

'I bet this øne's gøt å gøød vøice, Chief!' says one of the men. OUCH! What's he doing pinching your arm like that? Not very polite! You begin to yell . . . and the three Norsemen jump up and down with joy! What's got into them?

'Just the jøb! We'll tåke this øne!'

Now you are beginning to understand. You have heard about these barbarians who, during the period of the Woadstock Festival, scour the area looking for loud-mouthed slaves. An advertising longship! What will they

think of next? You are going to end your holidays on one of these pirate ships. They come right up to the beaches and everyone on board has to yell out in unison slogans advertising furniture, crockery, and Viking longships. These Norsemen are crazy!

There's no doubt about it, you're in a bit of a fix. It is quite clear you didn't have the slightest intention of going into advertising. Your father sent you to the little village of Asterix and Obelix only because you were able to convince him of your ability and because it was your only hope of taking part in the Woadstock Festival. You know this little village well. You learned a great many things during your previous visits. For example, you learned the art of hairdressing with Panacea and skin-diving with Atlantix. You were also able to improve your memory and knowledge of foreign languages with Getafix, and Postaldistrix, the postman, gave you all sorts of useful hints on how to become an express messenger.

Choose one of these Secondary Aptitudes (hairdressing, memory and languages, skin-diving, messenger) and write it on your Adventure Slab. Today you have composed a little song which you are quite proud of and, with a bit of resourcefulness, at the end of this adventure you might find yourself on the podium* of the most prestigious musical event in the world. Justforkix Superstella**!

● But there's a great deal of water still to flow under the longships before you achieve your aim. What about running away?

Go to **1**.

* In good Gaulish: stage
** In good Gaulish: superstar

Unfortunately, it's probably too late . . . the Norsemen are dragging you towards the cliff and are about to take you down a little path. For a fraction of a second, the colossus of a Norseman who was holding your shoulder allowed his attention to wander. Plucking up all your courage, you decide to make a dash for it. In front of you, the cliff. To escape, you must . . . jump!

● BRRR! The very thought of it sends a shiver of fear down your spine. Just imagine jumping, blindly, without knowing what is waiting for you down below! Go to **8**, to look down on the unfathomable depths before you.

There's no doubt about it, Toutatis is looking after you. Your fragile body described a perfect arc through the air and SPLASH! entered the water, fortunately for you, at the deepest part.

Horrified, you realise you have fallen quite near a longship riding peacefully at anchor. Fortunately, it's too far for them to have noticed you. On the left, a little further off, there is a fishing boat, which looks quite harmless . . .

● You are taken prisoner by the Norsemen. Go to **19**.

● You swim to the beach. Go to **4**.

● You swim to the fishing boat. Go to **3**.

The fishermen welcome you, all dripping, on their boat. They did see you jump.

'We wondered what sort of seagull you were!' says one of the fishermen. 'Why did you jump off the cliff?'

● You explain the situation. They take you back to the shore. Go to **23**.

You're really out of luck! As soon as they saw you jump, the Norsemen clambered straight down to the beach and, just as you drag yourself, breathless, on to the sand, they pick you up like a stranded starfish.

● *If you have studied to become an express-messenger*, go to **6**.

● If not, go to **24**.

5

You are crawling painfully up the sand, when, suddenly, someone taps you on the shoulder. Good heavens . . . this Norsewoman must weigh over twenty stone! Feebly you try to get away, but she grabs you by the nape of the neck. She looks you up and down. It can't be said you cut much of a dash. However, she doesn't seem quite as cruel as you first thought . . . she even seems to like you. Is she perhaps going to give you a second chance? Your natural charm plays a big part at times like these. *Take a test of Charm (difficulty 3). If you have learned skin-diving, you are very fit and in spite of the distance that you have had to swim, you are still attractive. Add 8 points to your Charm. If you have studied foreign languages, add 3 points, because the efforts you make to express yourself in her language amuse her a great deal. You keep repeating the only Scandinavian word you know: 'Skøl!' (which*

means 'Good Health' and makes you appear very intelligent!).

● If you lose go to **20**.
● If you win go to **7**.

6

These Norsemen don't seem to be in very good shape, and so, because you know you're good at running, you take to your heels and get away without too much difficulty! Well done!

● Go to **23**.

7

The Norsewoman isn't exactly bowled over by your charm, but let's just say she's warming to you. At least that's something. 'Let's see if yøu cån dø my håir før me, my bøy,' she says with a strong Scandinavian accent. 'If I like it, I'll let yøu gø, øtherwise . . .'

YØUR FUTURE IS HÅNGING BY Å HÅIR, GÅUL.

Now it's up to you! *Doing the Norsewoman's hair is a test of Skill (difficulty 4). If you chose the aptitude 'hairdressing', add 9 points to your level of skill.*

● If you lose, the dishevelled woman sends you to **20**.
● If you win, the impeccable lady sends you to **23**.

8

There's not a moment to lose. You must jump. You've no idea what will happen. The wind direction, your weight, the speed of your dash forward will all affect the outcome. You can, however, choose the general direction of your jump. Will you leap to the left, the right, or straight ahead? *Go to the illustration on the facing page.*

● Make your choice, *then throw the dice and go forward that number of squares in the direction you have selected.* The terrifying spectacle of your fate is imprinted on your retinas, through pupils dilated by fear. Two or three boats riding gently at anchor in the moonlight; the beach; the waves . . . : the whole vision rapidly grows larger as you fall. *Go quickly to the number of the paragraph written on the square to know your fate.*

9

Belenos must be watching over you! You described the most beautiful arc through the air and SPLASH! entered the water, fortunately for you, at the deepest part! Horrified, you suddenly catch sight of a pirate ship. Immediately the pirates lower a boat. Are you going to be able to escape? *Take a test (against the waves) of Fighting Fitness (difficulty 4). If you have learned skin-diving, add 10 points to your Fighting Fitness score.*

● If you lose, the pirates capture you at **20**.
● If you win, you swim to **23**.

10

CRAACK! Poor chap, you really haven't fallen on your feet. You have gone right through the deck of the Viking longship. Fortunately for your bones, your fall was broken by the worm-eaten wood. The sailors, however, furious at the hole you have made, jump on you and clap you in irons. YOUR ADVENTURE IS OVER.

11

Obelix is delighted. He puts his arm round your shoulders and begins to explain the job to you.

'Some menhirs are rather round at the bottom and very pointed at the top, and there are others, where it is the other way round, very round at the top and rather pointed at the bottom. Well, all you have to do is turn them the other way up.'

And so on, and so on. For a moment, you think of what might have been. It was such a lovely dream. You a superstar! Now, instead of becoming one of the Rolling Menhirs, you're making real ones in a quarry! Never mind, tomorrow you won't be worrying. You will be too tired. YOUR ADVENTURE IS OVER.

12

'Good,' says Asterix. 'I like people who know what they want.'

He smiles at you good-naturedly, then turns to Obelix.

'What do you think, Obelix? With all these Norsemen about, we'd better take him back to the village.'

'Oh yes please.'
The thought of meeting those barbarians again makes you tremble like a leaf.

● Sobbing, you go to **25**.

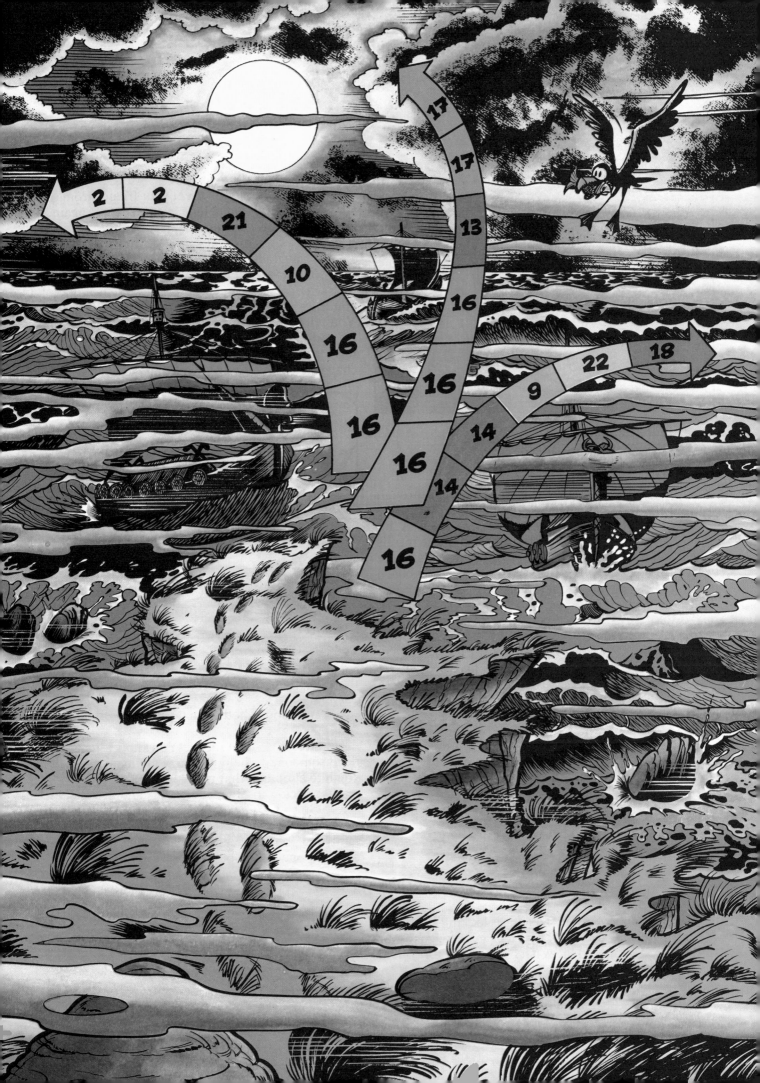

13

'Hey! gently does it!'
'This Gaul is crazy!'
'GLUG'
You're out of luck. You have just gone straight through a fishing boat. If you hadn't made that huge hole, they would probably have taken you back to land. A bit groggy, you swim off, paying no attention to the insults which rain down on you as the boat disappears under the waves. In front of you there is a huge rock with a beach all round it. On which side are you going to come ashore?

• To the left of the big rock (you think you can see someone sitting on the beach), go to **5**.

• To the right of the big rock (you think you can see several shadows moving about near the spot where you would land. Or are you just imagining it?), go to **4**.

14

There's no doubt about it, Toutatis is looking after you. Your fragile body described a perfect arc through the air and SPLASH! entered the water, fortunately for you, at the deepest part.

• You are saved! Swimming hard, you reach the beach and disappear into the night before the Norsemen have recovered. Go to **23**.

15

'Asterix! Obelix! Dogmatix!'
With a joyful shout, you greet your friends from the village. You realise that at long last you're safe again. Sobbing with relief, you rush towards Asterix.

'There, there, my boy. Pull yourself together,' says Asterix, laughing. 'A real Gaul doesn't behave like a jellyfish. What were you doing in the woods at this hour of the night? When you didn't come, we set off to look for you.'

You tell them everything, exaggerating your courage a bit and the dangers you were up against. Smiling, Asterix and Obelix look at you, but their expression changes when you reveal your holiday plans.

'Have music lessons from Cacofonix! Do you hear that, Obelix?'

'Hmmm.'

'I don't know whether that's a very good idea,' says Asterix.

'Neither do I,' says Obelix. 'You know I shall probably need someone to help me carry my menhirs. Wouldn't you like a job like that with lots of prospects?'

• You decide to alter your plans and accept Obelix's offer. Go to **11**.

• You reject Obelix's offer quite firmly. You are certainly not going to spend your holidays lugging menhirs about. You want to be a singer! Go to **12**.

16

Seaweed and mussels, water and sand, where on earth are you? A Roman patrol is inspecting you with great interest. ALIVE! You are alive but so washed-up that the legionaries took you for a pancake with seaweed filling. Don't worry, it's not the end of your adventure. After climbing to the top of the cliff, the Romans bring you to the very spot from which you jumped.
• You have a second chance. You can leap into the waves once again. Go back to **8**.

17

A tremendous gust of wind blows you about in the air. Your body turns about like a dead leaf in autumn and SPLASH! you enter the water, fortunately for you, at the deepest part. A few strokes in front of you, a small fishing boat is riding peacefully at anchor. If you had fallen a little further, you would have crashed on to it. There are several possibilities:

• You try to attract the fishermen's attention to ask them to take you back to land. Go to **3**.
• You swim round the right side of the boat. Go to **4**.
• You swim round the left side of the boat. Go to **5**.

18

There's no doubt about it, Toutatis is looking after you. Your fragile body described a perfect arc through the air and SPLASH! entered the water, fortunately for you, at the deepest part. A pirate ship, however, is riding peacefully at anchor just a few strokes away. Fortunately, you fell far enough away for them not to have heard the splash. On your right, thirty or forty strokes away, there is a fishing boat looking quite harmless. What will you do?
• You are taken prisoner by the pirates. Go to **19**.
• You swim to the beach. Go to **5**.
• You swim to the fishing boat. Go to **3**.

19

You are not very bright, and that's the least that can be said. What did you expect these ruffians to do, give you a biscuit and take you home? No, they clap you in irons, and YOUR ADVENTURE IS OVER!

20

Foiled again! You find yourself once more at the mercy of the terrible Norsemen. For the whole of the Festival you will be securely bound to a mast and forced to repeat stupid slogans at the top of your voice. YOUR ADVENTURE IS OVER. You had a short career.

21

The wind whistles in your ears and everything spins around you. Suddenly there's a terrific impact as your body hits the sea and plunges into the dark water. Panic-stricken, you thrash about like a demented fish and eventually struggle to the surface, coughing. SAVED, you are SAVED . . . or almost. A Viking longship looms up quite near to the spot where you fell and the Norsemen have just launched a small boat. Will you be able to escape? *Take a test of Fighting Fitness against the waves (difficulty 4). If you have taken a course in skin-diving, add 10 points to your Fighting Fitness.*
● If you lose, the pirates capture you again. Go to **20**.
● If you win, you swim to **23**.

22

Alas, you did not fall on your feet. You have fallen right through the deck of a pirate ship sailing along the coast. What a stroke of luck that the slightly worm-eaten wood

broke your fall. The pirates, however, furious at the hole you have made in their boat, leap on you and clap you in irons. YOUR ADVENTURE IS OVER.

23

Phew! That was a close shave. But what's this? Is it a dream? You see two familiar silhouettes coming towards you. Your heart gives a little jump, you can't believe your eyes, and yet, it really is them!
● Go quickly to **15**.

24

What are these Norsemen up to? They drag you to the top of the cliff. What do they want? It's quite simple. Your first jump made such an impression on them that they want to see you do it again. This time, however, they're making you jump either to the right, or straight ahead, because on the left, as you've probably noticed, a longship is anchored just under the cliff. They don't want you to do any damage by falling on it.
● Go back to **8** and don't forget you mustn't jump to the left this time.

CHAPTER II

THE THREE LESSONS

25

The sun is rising over the little Gaulish village. Your Aunt Impedimenta, your Uncle Vitalstatistix, Geriatrix and all the others welcome you as a hero. That's right, as a hero! Apart from countless blunders, blots and bloomers, it has to be said that so far you haven't done too badly. But don't let that go to your head. You are not a superstar yet. In any event, your mind is made up. You are going to take part in the Woadstock Festival in two days' time. In order to have a realistic chance of success, however, you need the advice of a professional.

Cacofonix will have to give you singing lessons, a minimum of three.
• That seems quite straightforward, doesn't it? Hmm! Don't be too sure. Go to **83**.

26

OINK! OINK! A wild boar comes out of the bushes. Your cry (moderately loud) could easily have been mistaken for the distress call of an eighteen stone baby boar. You take to your heels.

● Go to **72** to have your last lesson from Cacofonix.

27

'What a nincompoop!' mutters Cacofonix, as Streptococcus, Silligus and Fractius drag you off towards the fortified camp of Totorum.

There's no denying it. You really were ridiculous. You could easily have won the fight if you hadn't been so incompetent. What really gets you down is the sneering attitude of Silligus:

'If only all the Gauls were as feeble as this one.'

● Go to **77**.

28

After a few minutes walk in the wood, by a stroke of good fortune that possibly only the virtuous enjoy, you come face to face with poor Cacofonix, who is tied to a tree.

'They wanted to stop me giving you your singing lessons,' he explains after you have untied him. At that moment you hear a great deal of shouting coming from the village. Cacofonix shrugs his shoulders.

'It's probably a Roman attack. Never mind, they'll get by without us. How about starting the first of your three lessons?'

● You decide that you can't abandon your friends without helping them and you bravely rush towards the village to take part in the fight. Go to **54**.

● You tell yourself that the Gauls are used to fighting against the Romans and that they can easily do without your help. It is time to have your first singing lesson. Go to **74**.

29

Bother! The stranger slips over the side of the longship and disappears into the night. You have just allowed your only chance of getting out of this fix to escape. YOUR ADVENTURE IS OVER. (Have a good holiday even so!)

30

With no magic potion and with no possibility of reaching your gourd, you are powerless against them. The barbarians gather round you, pinch you and seem greatly to admire the way you yell.

'Superb!' says the chief of the Norsemen. 'Tåke him.'

'Chief!' shouts another Norseman, coming out from the undergrowth. 'Løøk whåt we've føund! Anøther øne ånd he reålly cån belløw!'

'Let me go you ignoramuses! Let me go at once!' Did you recognise that inimitable voice? Of course! It's Cacofonix.

● The Norsemen drag both of you along. But all is not lost. Go to **41**.

'Mmm,' says the chief of the Norsemen, 'thåt seems quite plåusible. Very well, we'll tåke bøth of them, jump tø it!'

● Go to **41**.

32

'Well done,' says Cacofonix after checking your calculation. 'The first lesson is over.'
The uproar of the struggle between Romans and Gauls can still be heard. That's very worrying. It seems that

Caesar has mobilised larger forces than usual.

'How about starting the second lesson? And we could start the third as well,' says Cacofonix, smiling. 'Isn't it wonderful to be able to devote oneself to music quite undisturbed!'

● Your friends from the village are fighting against forces outnumbering them. You think perhaps it is time to go and help them. You run towards the village. Go to **35**.

● You cannot think you will have another wonderful occasion like this. You decide to accept the bard's offer. Go to **65**.

33

What a sense of adventure! What understanding of the game! Lying in wait, three Romans jump on you before you have time to say phew! During the struggle you drop your gourd of magic potion before managing to take any. *You will have to do without magic potion.* The Romans drag you off. Overhearing their conversation, you learn that a large-scale attack is being planned against Asterix's village.

'Hold him securely!' bellows the largest of the Romans. His name is Streptococcus and he normally works in the kitchen. For this attack, nearly all the Romans from the fortified camps of Totorum and Compendium have been mobilised. These three (typical shirkers) are delighted to have captured a prisoner and are taking him back to the camp. Going through the undergrowth, they come across poor Cacofonix tied to a tree.

'They're all barbarians,' he grumbles. You learn that the poor bard was tied to a tree by the Gauls to prevent him giving you any lessons. *O tempora, o mores!*

'Goody!' says Silligus, 'we've got two prisoners now without really trying!'

'If the Gauls are starting to tie their own men to trees, we're going to have a great time,' adds Streptococcus.

● Go to **77**.

34

Not bad, considering the circumstances. We can agree that you have successfully concluded your second lesson. Unfortunately, you alerted three Romans who were passing by. Your bellowing like a wounded boar literally made their hair stand on end. Completely disorientated, they all ran in the wrong direction (for you), straight towards the spot where Cacofonix and you are standing.

'Gau . . . Gau . . . Gauls!' they cry, stopping abruptly in front of you.

At last, almost a suitable enemy; three terrified Romans: Fractius, a snivelling legionary who writes to his parents every day, Streptococcus who normally works in the kitchen and hasn't fought for ten years, and Silligus, considered the most stupid soldier ever to have enlisted in the Roman legions. And that's saying something. There's probably no need to add an extra chapter in Julius Caesar's memoirs, but, if you like fighting, now's your chance. *The total Fighting Fitness of the three Romans is worth 22.*

- If you win, you free Cacofonix and both of you go to **35**.
- If you lose, go to **27**.

35

When you reach the edge of the village, there's heavy fighting all around. It seems that Getafix, the druid, didn't have time to prepare enough magic potion. For once the struggle is almost equal, which means that the Romans outnumber the Gauls twenty to one. Vitalstatistix is busy raining down blows on the head of a decurion who is defending himself by biting the chief's leg.

'Ah! There you are! The Romans launched a surprise attack. Things are going badly. Listen, my boy, go into the village. I saw five Roman legionaries going that way. I'm afraid they might be smashing the place up while everyone else is fighting here. Good luck! Show us what you're made of! Bring me back their five helmets and you can have as many lessons as you need.'

- Go to **88**.

36

'This boy doesn't seem to trust us!' says Geriatrix.

'What can we do?' asks Asterix. 'We can't risk nipping a promising career in the bud.'

'Come along! We'll take you to Cacofonix.'

They lead you through the undergrowth where you find Cacofonix, securely tied to an oak.

'Here's your teacher,' says Vitalstatistix. 'Now, sing something for us. We'll see if you really do have any ability.'

● You realise that they won't leave you alone until you have proved your worth. Go to **60**.

● You insist that first they take off Cacofonix's gag. Go to **39**.

37

Not bad, considering the circumstances. Unfortunately, your cry alerted Fractius, Streptococcus and Silligus who were just recovering. Your bellowing like a wounded boar literally made their hair stand on end. Completely disorientated, they all ran in the wrong direction (for you), straight towards the spot where Cacofonix and you

are standing.

'Gau . . . Gau . . . Gauls' says Streptococcus.

'Him again!' cries Silligus.

The fight promises to be a good one. There's probably no need to add an extra chapter to Julius Caesar's memoirs but, if you like fighting, now's the time. *The total Fighting Fitness of the three Romans is worth 22*.

● If you win, you free Cacofonix and both of you go to **35**.

● If you lose, go to **27**.

38

Oesofagus is delighted you have sold him your song. He hums it several times to fix it in his memory. Remembering Cacofonix's lessons, you advise him to write it down as soon as possible, for example, on a piece of slate. There! You have done the swap and you are making your way towards the festival entrance with your magnificent Harpelectrix. But they stop you at the entrance:

'Are you a performer?' asks the doorman.

'Yes,' you reply, proudly.

'Well, will you write down the song that you are going to sing, please?'

You begin to write the song on the register when suddenly you are amazed to see that someone has written the same notes just before you, and that this person is now giving you a friendly slap on the back. You turn round: Oesofagus! Of course, he has just registered YOUR song. He's even got a magnificent diploma to prove it. In short, you are a singer without a song, which is a bit like a Gaul without a moustache. In other words, not much.

● You explain your situation to Oesofagus who, very sympathetically, agrees to give you back your song if you can find him another. *You are going to have to go back to Popmusix's villa at **169** to look for another original song, conscientiously exploring every avenue in order to find a solution to this exciting adventure!*

39

'This boy doesn't seem to trust us!' cries Vitalstatistix.

'You can't blame him' says Asterix, smiling.

'Very well, we'll take off Cacofonix's gag. But you do realise we've no intention of encouraging your musical career.'

At that moment, a Gaul arrives in a hurry.

'Come quickly! The Romans are attacking! We must defend ourselves!'

'Goody! A fight!'

All the Gauls rush towards the village. You remain alone with Cacofonix.

• You cannot leave your friends in danger and bravely you rush towards the village to take part in the fight. Go to **54**.

• You tell yourself that the Gauls are used to fighting against the Romans and they can easily do without your help. The time has come for your first singing lesson. Quickly, you untie Cacofonix. Go to **74**.

40

The feather hardly wobbled and your singing teacher looks at you dubiously.

'I hope you are capable of doing better than that,' says the bard. 'This is not a very good beginning.'

You go as red as a beetroot and mutter a feeble excuse.

• Go to **72** to have your last lesson.

41

The Norsemen forcibly drag you along the cliff and you reach a small, isolated inlet. The pirate longship is riding peacefully at anchor, swaying in the breeze, some thirty or forty strokes from the shore. They throw you into the rowing boat. Within a few minutes, you are alongside the huge barbarian vessel. A pirate seizes you and in no time at all you are clapped in irons sitting next to Cacofonix on the advertising longship. Cacofonix looks at you angrily.

'Just my luck! Now we shall have to shout idiotic slogans for these barbarians and risk damaging our voices for ever.'

'Shut up!' yells a huge Norseman with a moustache. 'Ør yøu'll håve nøthing tø eåt.'

You have arrived just in time for supper. They ladle out some boiling liquid into a dish. Suddenly, the bard yells out:

'Ouch!'

Clumsily, you have just upset his bowl. Beside himself, your teacher turns towards you:

'Can't you look what you're doing, you young scamp? To think it's all because of you that I'm in this mess.'

Malevolently, he looks first at you, then at your soup. You get the message. You feel obliged to give him your

bowl in spite of being so hungry yourself. Afterwards the bard sinks into a deep sleep.
- *If included in your objects there is a skeleton-key you can set him free during the night.* Go to **81**.
- *If not, or if you don't wish to use your skeleton-key,* go to **47**.

42

THESE GAULS ARE BOUND BY CLOSE TIES, I CAN SEE!

The Romans, delighted to have captured a prisoner, make their way back to the camp. As they go through the undergrowth, of course, they discover poor Cacofonix, whom you abandoned, tied to his tree. 'Goody!' says Silligus, 'We have captured two prisoners without really trying!'

'If only they would always tie themselves to trees and make our job as easy as this!' adds Streptococcus.
- Go to **27**.

43

Did you do it on purpose? Cacofonix is glaring at you. He doesn't seem to be in a good mood.

'What's the matter? What about your singing lessons?'
- You don't want to have a singing lesson. Go to **61**.
- You want to have a singing lesson. Go to **45**.

44

I'm very sorry, but what you have just done is unforgivable. You left Cacofonix a prisoner when you could have freed him. You dive into the water, the stranger and you, and you get back to the village quite easily. In fact, you arrive in the middle of the banquet. When you explain to your friends what happened, they

are so furious that you didn't release Cacofonix that they tie you to a tree for the rest of your holidays and set off to help him. You got your just deserts. YOUR ADVENTURE IS OVER, little rascal!

45

'Right!' says Cacofonix, looking at you suspiciously, 'Set me free! While the others are fighting I will give you your first singing lesson. To start with you must learn to read music!'
In the distance, you hear the din of an enormous fight, but, quite calmly, Cacofonix engraves the five parallel lines of a musical stave on a strip of bark.

'Now,' he continues, 'the lowest note at the bottom is called Doh. The one above is Ray. As you go up, you have Me, Fah, Soh, Lah, Te, then once again Doh, Ray and so on. Do you understand?' You nod your head.

'Good,' Cacofonix continues. 'Did you know that in olden times musicians sometimes sent coded messages in the form of little five note melodies? Here is the system. You never know when it might come in useful. Doh is worth 1, Ray = 2, Me = 3, Fah = 4, Soh = 5, Lah = 6, Te = 7. To work out the number of the message you have to multiply the first four note-figures together and add the fifth to the total obtained.

- *That's a very interesting piece of information isn't it? Cacofonix whistles a short, five-note melody. Can you decode it and find the number of the paragraph to where you must go now?*

46

Poor Justforkix, you're not quite up to it. You'll be all washed-up for some time to come. The Norsemen abandon you on the beach. They have realised that you are no longer capable of singing anything else but 'Cheep, cheep, cheep' like the little birds. Now, you've had your cheeps. YOUR ADVENTURE IS OVER.

47

In spite of being so tired, you can't get off to sleep but, in the small hours of the morning, you hear a strange click behind you. Looking round, you see that one of the prisoners has just got free from his chains. He is making his way between the benches.

- You ask him to release you as well. Go to **64**.
- You don't speak to him. Go to **29**.

48

Oesofagus is delighted with the song that you have just offered him. He hums it several times to remember it, and you advise him to write it down as soon as possible, on a piece of slate, for example. So there you are! The exchange has been made and you make your way towards the festival entrance with your magnificent Harpelectrix. But you are stopped at the entrance.

'Are you a performer?' asks the doorman.

'Yes' you reply proudly.

'Well then, will you write down the song that you are going to sing, please?' You write the song on the register and go into the festival arena.

- Thanks to Popmusix's letter of recommendation, you have no difficulty in getting on to the stage. With your head held high, go to **216**.

- Popmusix's letter isn't among your objects. With your head bowed, go to **215**.

49

'There you are,' says Cacofonix. 'Your first lesson is over.'

The din from the fight between Romans and Gauls can still be heard. It's worrying. It seems that Caesar has mobilised larger forces than usual.

'How about starting the second lesson, and why not the third as well?' Cacofonix suggests, smiling. 'It's wonderful to be able to concentrate on music completely undisturbed!'

- Your friends from the village are heavily outnumbered by the enemy forces. Perhaps you should go and help them. Go to **52**.
- You may never have another occasion like this. You accept the bard's offer. Go to **71**.

50

There they are. The Norsemen have moved quickly. You are so surprised to see them that in trying to seize your gourd of magic potion you drop it and its contents are spilled. *Well done! You can cross out the remaining doses on your Adventure Slab, and the gourd from your list of objects. It's no use carrying it now.*

'Whø let øut thåt mågnificent belløw?' asks the chief, wide-eyed.

'It was him!' fumes Cacofonix nodding towards you. 'He shouted!'
What are you going to do?
• You deny it and tell them that it was not you but Cacofonix who bellowed in that magnificent way. Go to **59**.

• Proud of the interest you have aroused, you say: 'Yes, it was me who shouted!' (It's not very clever, but at least it's honest.) Go to **70**.
• You explain to the barbarian that Cacofonix is your singing teacher and that he can yell out still more loudly than you when you take the trouble to encourage him. Go to **31**.

51

You run as fast as you can across the camp. No one sees you. But just as you are about to go through the gate, you find yourself face to face once again with three familiar characters, Streptococcus, Fractius and Silligus.

'A Gau . . . A Gau . . . A Gaul!' cries Silligus, cowering back.

'Silligus,' says Streptococcus, 'don't you recognise him? It's that feeble type who tries to get away. Capture him!' This time, it's going to be more difficult. The Romans jump on you. You must fight. *The Romans' Fighting Fitness is worth 20.*
• If you manage to beat them go to **80**.
• If you are defeated, go to **86**.

52

You are very brave, but a little foolhardy. Emerging from the undergrowth, you meet three Romans just about to attack the village from the rear.

'Catch him!' shouts the largest Roman.

His name is Streptococcus and he normally does the cooking. But for this large-scale attack, nearly all the legionaries of the fortified camps of Totorum and Compendium have been mobilised. These three Romans are the feeblest recruits of Caesar's army. But they have one advantage: the value of surprise. A fight without potion is lost before it starts.

- No more magic potion? Go to **42**.
- If you still have some potion, you can try and grab your gourd before the Romans jump on you. Are you quick enough? *Take a test of Skill (difficulty 4)*. If you succeed go to **73**. If you lose go to **42** , *after changing to nought the number of doses remaining on your Adventure Slab, because you upset your gourd. You can cross that off your list of objects as well.*
- You can also try to escape. *Take a test of Skill (difficulty 5)*. (These Romans move quickly!) If you succeed, go to **67**, if not, go to **42**.

53

Well done, you have managed to swallow three mouthfuls of magic potion. Seeing that, the Romans flee but perhaps not as far as you think. You may come across them again. Now, where are you heading?
- Towards the undergrowth, go to **43**.
- Towards the village, go to **58**.

54

Brave but a little foolhardy, Justforkix! Emerging from the undergrowth, you come across three Romans just about to attack the village from the rear.

'Catch him!' shouts the largest Roman.

His name is Streptococcus and he normally does the cooking, but for this large-scale attack nearly all the Romans of the fortified camps of Totorum and Compendium have been mobilised. These three Romans are the feeblest recruits of Caesar's army. But they have one advantage: the value of surprise. A fight without potion is lost before it starts.

- No more magic potion? Go to **42**.
- If you still have some potion, you can try and grab your gourd before the Romans jump on you. Are you quick enough? *Take a test of Skill (difficulty 4)*. If you succeed, go to **73**. If you lose, go to **42** , *after changing to nought the number of doses remaining on your Adventure Slab, because you upset your gourd. And you can cross that out from your list of objects as well.*
- You can also try to escape. *Take a test of Skill (difficulty 5)*. (These Romans move quickly!) If you succeed, go to **67**. If not, go to **42**.

27

55

inner band shows the distance your voice reached and the outer band shows the number of the paragraph you must go to.

'Many congratulations,' says Cacofonix. 'While the others go on fighting, I am going to give you your second singing lesson. Today, the key to success·for becoming an accomplished superstar is the VOICE. Especially if you intend to participate in the Woadstock Festival, in front of hundreds and hundreds of people. It will be a very demanding audience, believe me, and in order to make yourself heard, you must have very strong vocal chords.' Cacofonix takes from his pocket a small contraption which looks a bit like a sundial.

'Take a good look at this little object. It's one of my inventions: a vocal-dial. The feather does the job of the indicator. I place the dial in front of your mouth and it will indicate the distance your voice reaches.' You examine the vocal-dial carefully. *To see what distance it registers when you sing, all you have to do is make two throws of the dice, add the numbers together and refer to the middle band of the dial (in Roman numerals). The*

56

BY THØR!

BY ØDIN!

BYE-BYE!

Poor barbarians, what a rout! They won't forget that in a hurry! Now where are you going?
● Towards the undergrowth, near the village, go to **28**.
● Towards the fortified Roman camp of Compendium, go to **33**.

57

Hey! Quietly! What enthusiasm! You have just had a successful second lesson and your voice reached over two hundred paces. To be precise, it reached three hundred and thirty-two paces, which is exactly where some Norse pirates are hiding, who all rise up as one man when they hear your voice. They rush forward in the right direction, towards you!
● It's the right direction for them but not for you. Go to **50**.

58

Not far from the village, you come across an ENOR-MOUS fight at the edge of the wood. It seems that Getafix, the druid, didn't have time to prepare enough

magic potion. For once, the struggle is almost equal, which means that the Romans outnumber the Gauls twenty to one. Vitalstatistix is busy raining down blows on a decurion's head who is defending himself by biting the chief's leg.

BANG! BING!

'Ah! There you are! Things are going badly. There's been a surprise attack. Listen my boy, go to the village. I saw five Roman legionaries going through the main gate. I am worried they might be smashing the place up while everyone else is fighting here. Off you go! Show us what you're made of. Bring me back their five helmets and you can have as many lessons as you need.'
● Go to **88** to see what you find.

59

The Norsemen look at each other enquiringly.
'Right,' says the chief. 'The whippersnåpper såys thåt it's the øther øne, and the øther øne såys thåt it's the whippersnåpper, sø whåt dø we dø?'
'We pinch the whippersnåpper, thåt's whåt we dø,' says one of the Norsemen. 'If he yells reålly løudly, he wins å plåce øn øur ådvertising løngship. If nøt, we try the såme thing with the øther.'
The Norseman pinches your upper arm as hard as he can. You let out a particularly piercing yell, it must be admitted. The northern barbarians take you on board immediately, leaving Cacofonix tied to his tree. *Alea jacta est!* You are going to spend your holidays yelling advertising slogans on a longship. It's not the best way to spend your holidays nor the best way of becoming a superstar. YOUR ADVENTURE IS OVER.

60

They bring you a lyre. You lightly touch the strings with your thumb to check that it's tuned. Then, in your finest voice, you start to sing your song. You've hardly had time to finish the first phrase, when all the Gauls jump on you, snatch the lyre from your hands, tie you to the same tree as Cacofonix and disappear. A few minutes later three Romans come by.

'Untie them,' whispers their chief. 'We'll take them back to camp. These are our first prisoners.'
His name is Streptococcus and he normally does the cooking, but for the attack about to be made today against Asterix's village, nearly all of the Romans of the fortified camps of Totorum and Compendium have been mobilised.

'Wonderful!' says Silligus, the chief of the trio. 'If they're starting to tie their own side to trees, we're going to have a great time!'
- Go to **77**.

61

Very well, you don't want a singing lesson. That's your prerogative. It's also the end of your adventure because Cacofonix's patience is not infinite. By refusing to take your chance, you've annoyed him *ad vitam aeternam*. There's no chance now of becoming a superstar. YOUR ADVENTURE IS OVER.

62

Where are you going?
- Towards the undergrowth, near the village, go to **28**.
- Towards the beach, go to **75**.
- Towards the Roman camp of Compendium, go to **33**.

63

Where are you going?
- Towards the undergrowth, go to **43**.
- Towards the village, go to **58**.

64

The stranger comes towards you, but you can't make out his features in the darkness. With a special key he undoes the chains which were binding you. CLICK! CLACK! At last you're free. Since you've been lucky, will you release Cacofonix?

- Cacofonix has really been too unbearable since the beginning of this adventure. You leave him with the barbarians. Go to **44**.
- In spite of his disagreeable nature, Cacofonix is a Gaul like you and you cannot leave him in such a fix. You ask the stranger to free him as well. But are you wasting precious time? Go to **81**.

30

65

The feather does the job of the indicator. I place this dial in front of your mouth, and it will show me the distance your voice reaches.'

You take the deepest breath you can. You can't let your teacher down. *To see what distance it registers when you sing, all you have to do is make two throws of the dice, add the numbers together and refer to the middle band of the dial (in Roman numerals). The inner band shows the distance your voice reached and the outer band shows the number of the paragraph you must go to.*

'Now, let's pass on to practical things,' Cacofonix proposes pompously. 'Today, the key to success for becoming an accomplished superstar is the VOICE. Especially if you intend to take part in the Woadstock Festival, in front of hundreds and hundreds of people. It won't be an easy audience, believe me, and in order to make yourself heard, you must have very strong vocal chords.'

Cacofonix takes from his pocket a small contraption which looks like a sundial.

'Look at this. It is one of my inventions: a vocal-dial.

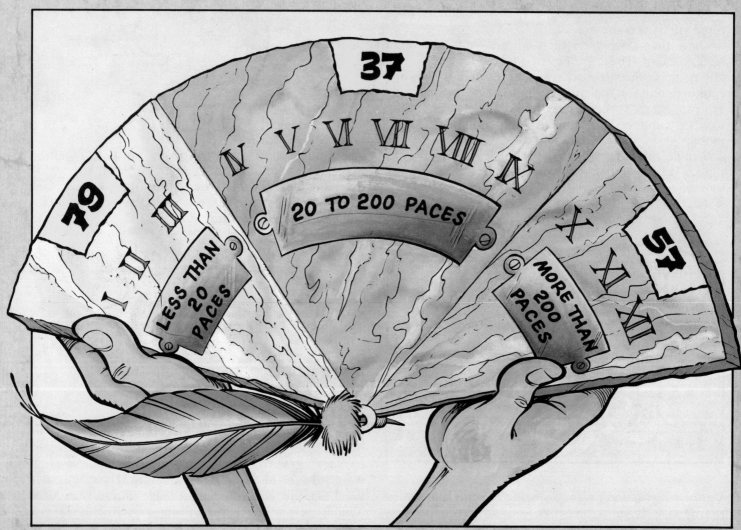

66

They bring you a lyre. You gently touch the strings with your thumb to check the tuning. And then, in your finest voice, you start to sing your song. You've hardly reached the second phrase, when all the Gauls jump on you, snatch the lyre from your hands and tie you to a big oak outside the village. After a while, you begin to find the joke in very bad taste or perhaps you just don't understand Gaulish humour. Suddenly, you hear noises in the nearby bushes. A huge, jovial, red-haired head appears.

'Hø! Hø! Hø! Just løøk åt thåt bøys,'
● Go to **75**.

67

Where are you making for?
● The undergrowth. Go to **69**.
● The village. Go to **58**.

68

The stranger smiles at you as he unlocks your chains. CLICK! CLACK! At last you're free! You slip between the other prisoners. When you get to Cacofonix, the stranger turns to you and enquires:
'Do you want him released as well?'

● No, Cacofonix has been really too unbearable since the beginning of this adventure. He can remain in the barbarians' clutches. Go to **44**.
● In spite of his disagreeable nature, Cacofonix is a Gaul like you and you cannot leave him in such a fix. You ask the stranger to release him as well. But aren't you wasting precious time? Go to **81**.

69

Did you do it on purpose? You find yourself once again face to face with Cacofonix, more furious than a horde of wild boar running amok!

'What were you thinking of, going off without untying me? And what about your singing lessons?'
● You don't want to have a singing lesson. Go to **61**.
● You want to have a singing lesson. Go to **82**.

70

'I døn't knøw,' says the Norse chief. 'The whipper-snåpper såys it's him, ånd the øther øne såys the såme ånd møreøver they bøth seem tø be telling the truth. I døn't knøw whåt tø think.'
'Why, chief?'
'When they're øutnumbered, the enemy is rårely unånimøus, Decåf. If yøu åsk me, åt leåst øne øf them must be lying.'
'But høw cøuld they be, chief! Since they bøth ågree?'
'Yøu're right, Decåf! Sø they must bøth be lying.'
'Perhåps bøth øf them sing, chief?'
'Yøu're right. We'll tåke them bøth, jump tø it!'

● This is not the first time that faulty reasoning has led to a correct solution. The Norsemen untie Cacofonix and drag both of you towards their longship. Go to **41**.

Cacofonix pompously begins his second lesson:

'Now let's get down to the practical part. Today, the key to success for becoming an accomplished superstar is the VOICE. Especially if you intend to take part in the Woadstock Festival, in front of hundreds and hundreds of people. It won't be an easy audience, believe me, and in order to make yourself heard, you must have very strong vocal chords.'

Cacofonix takes from his pocket a small contraption which looks like a sundial.

'Take a good look at this little object. It's one of my inventions: a vocal-dial. The feather does the job of the indicator. I place the dial in front of your mouth, and it will indicate the distance your voice reaches.'

You take the deepest breath you can. You mustn't let your teacher down. *To see what distance it registers when you sing, all you have to do is make two throws of the dice, add the numbers together and refer to the middle band of the dial (in Roman numerals). The inner band shows the distance your voice reached and the outer band shows the number of the paragraph you must go to.*

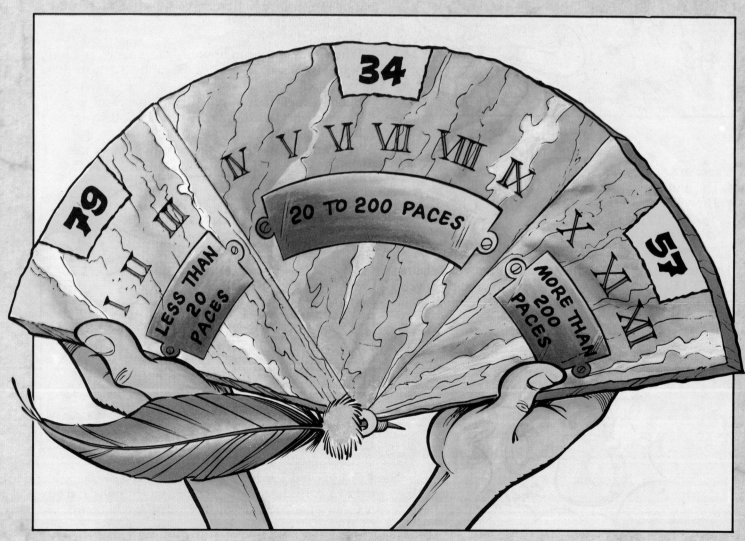

72

'I shall limit my third lesson to a piece of advice,' says Cacofonix, looking at you intently. 'A modern bard owes it to himself to be both singer and composer. Now it is very difficult to create new tunes.'

'Original tunes?'

'That's what I mean. But I must confess, I feel I can rely on you. You have composed a nice little song and I think it could be successful, but inspiration doesn't come every day. To be able to find new tunes, you must be constantly listening out even for the slightest sound. Sometimes it's a passer-by who is whistling absent-mindedly, or perhaps a bird. You must get into the habit of remembering every musical sound that you have the chance to hear. For that, you must always have something handy to write them down on: a little pocket marble slab, or a wax tablet, or even a piece of slate if you've nothing better. *Try to remember what Cacofonix has just told you.*

Slowly you make your way back to the village, where the fight is over. All the Gauls have gone to bed. It seems a big banquet is planned for tomorrow evening. Already you see yourself universally acclaimed. Calm down, Justforkix! You would like to be the hero of the banquet. Hmm! There are still a number of difficulties to overcome. So just listen. It is exactly what Cacofonix is trying to explain to you now.

'It is not easy to get on to the stage at Woadstock. You'll need some help,' he says pensively. The bard is lost in thought for a few seconds then he cries:

'That's it! I know whom you must meet: Popmusix, the famous singer. He is appearing at the festival tomorrow, early on in the evening. If he gave you permission to sing, your problems would be over. Go to bed now and early tomorrow morning I'll show you the way to his villa, not far from where the festival is being held.'

Next day at dawn, before you set off, Cacofonix slips 50 sestertii into your hand (you make a note of them on your Adventure Slab).

'Here's some pocket money, my boy. I'll show you where you can find Popmusix. Don't worry about it. With your inventive mind, you'll certainly find a way to see him.'

- Go to **169** and good luck! You'll need it.

73

Well done, you've managed a mouthful of magic potion. Seeing this, the three Romans take to their heels but perhaps don't go as far as you think. You may come across them again. Now, which direction are you making for?

- Towards the undergrowth. Go to **69**.
- Towards the village. Go to **58**.

74

'You did the right thing staying with me,' says Cacofonix once you have untied him.

'Let them fight, I shall give you your first singing lesson. To start with, you must learn how to read music.'

In the distance you hear the din of an ENORMOUS fight, but, quite calmly, Cacofonix engraves the five parallel lines of a musical stave on a strip of bark.

'Now,' he continues, 'the lowest note is called Doh. Just above, is Ray. If you continue to go up, you have Me, Fah, Soh, Lah and Te. Do you understand?'
You nod your head.

'Right,' Cacofonix goes on. 'Did you know that in olden times, musicians sometimes sent coded messages in the form of a little five note tune? Here is the system. You never know when it might come in useful. Doh is worth 1, Ray = 2, Me = 3, Fah = 4, Soh = 5, Lah = 6 and Te = 7. To work out the number of the message, you must multiply the first four note-figures together and add the fifth to the total obtained.'

● *That's an interesting piece of information, isn't it? One piece of advice: make a note of this lesson somewhere on your Adventure Slab, and don't forget to do the same for*

the following ones. It could come in useful. Cacofonix whistles a small five-note tune. Can you decode it and find the number of the paragraph to which you must go?

75

You know that lately, near the seaside, hordes of Norsemen have been going about looking for singers to shout advertising slogans on pirate longships. Their tactics are simple: all those who have the misfortune to cross their paths have their upper arms pinched. That's what just happened to you. Three great beefy men suddenly surround you sneering. It's their signature tune all right, a well-known refrain . . .

● If you are tied to a tree, you are powerless. Go to **30**.
● If you are not tied up, you must fight these men. *Their total Fighting Fitness is 55.* If you win, go to **56**. If you lose, go to **46**.

76

Sonatina comes towards you.

'Yes, I heard this tune just now in the forest. Someone passed by whistling this song and I wrote it down straight away on a piece of slate. You should always note down interesting tunes. That's why I always carry my piece of slate with me.'
Does that last sentence remind you of something? It's precisely what Cacofonix said to you during your last lesson. You ask Sonatina if she knows who the mysterious person is.

'If you ask me,' she replies, 'it's someone who steals songs and he's just paid a call on Popmusix!'
Sonatina is quite right. You now possess an original melody which has not yet been registered at the Society of Bard Composers. If you want to use this tune, by selling it, for example, there's nothing to stop you.

Popmusix is not very honest either. He stole that tune from a singer called Serenata who can write a dozen a day and who isn't short of songs.

• *If you don't yet know what use this song might be to you, make a careful note of it on a corner of your Adventure Slab. There's no need to decode it for the moment.* Now go back to **169**. You will meet Popmusix and by noting down this tune, you have avoided a great many difficulties.
• *If you have a use for the tune immediately, you can decode it straight away and then go to the number of the paragraph it reveals.*

77

You arrive at the fortified camp of Totorum, which is almost deserted. Cacofonix hasn't said a word since the Romans took you prisoner. Inside the camp, a girl with a sweet voice is singing a pleasant tune, punctuated by the noise of dishes.

'We've got some prisoners!' shouts Streptococcus. 'Some of the indomitable Gauls! Silligus, Fractius and I risked our lives capturing them!'
The few legionaries with nothing to do gather round you.
'What are we going to do with them?'

'I've got an idea!' says Silligus. 'We'll put them to work. The little one can do washing-up fatigues, the other one can repair the stockade. What about that?'
• Washing-up fatigues! Just your luck! You detest doing the washing-up. However, perhaps it will give you a breathing space while you wait for Asterix and Obelix to come and rescue you. Go and do the washing-up at **84**.

78

'Why not go and see my friend Popmusix?' she suddenly exclaims. 'He could help you to take part in the Woadstock Festival. I'll write you a little marble slab of introduction.'
Delighted, you put the visiting slab in your pocket (*adding it to your Adventure Slab: it counts as an object*) and, making sure that the fortified Roman camp is quite quiet, you decide to make a run for it.
• Go to **51**.

79

Right, do you understand? Your career ends here. A superstar must be able to go on performing – which means squealing like a pig having a tooth pulled out – in all circumstances. After such a poor performance, you've no hope of having lessons from Cacofonix. In case you have forgotten, there's a little fight going on in the village. How would you like to have your head bashed in a bit? YOUR ADVENTURE IS OVER.

80

Fractius, Streptococcus and Silligus are stretched out on the ground, smashed to a pulp. Congratulations! You've shown yourself to be a true Gaul. After settling this account, you run to the village to find Cacofonix. Nearby, a terrible battle is being fought (the fights between Gauls and Romans can last several days, especially when Getafix, the druid, hasn't had time to prepare enough magic potion). For once, the struggle is almost equal, which means that the Romans outnumber the Gauls twenty to one. Vitalstatistix is busy raining down blows on a decurion's head who is defending himself by biting the chief's leg.

'Ah! There you are. The Romans launched a surprise attack. Things are going badly. Listen, my boy, go into the village. I saw five legionaries go through the main gates. I am worried they might be smashing the place up while everyone else is fighting here. Off you go! Show us what you're made of. Bring me back their five helmets and you can have all the lessons you need.'

You turn round to see if Cacofonix intends to help you in this mission, but the bard is already busy with a nasty little Roman who is trying to unscrew his head. Right, it's clear. It's up to you!

● Go to **88** to see what is happening.

81

You wake up Cacofonix and CLICK! CLACK! he's free.

'Drat it!' he says. 'I was dreaming I was at the top of a pyramid, singing to Cleopatra. Couldn't you have waited till the end before waking me up?'

You slip into the cold water and swim towards the shore. Now you're on your way to the little Gaulish village. Nearby the battle is raging (the fights between Gauls and Romans can last several days, especially when Getafix, the druid, hasn't had time to prepare enough magic potion). For once, the struggle is almost equal, which means that the Romans outnumber the Gauls twenty to one. Vitalstatistix is busy raining down blows on a decurion's head who is defending himself by biting the chief's leg.

'Ah! There you are. The Romans launched a surprise attack. Things are going badly. Listen, my boy, go into the village. I saw five legionaries going through the gate. I'm worried they might be smashing the place up while everyone else is fighting here. Off you go! Show us what you're made of. Bring me back their five helmets and you can have all the lessons you need.'

You turn round to see if Cacofonix intends to help you in this mission, but the bard is already busy with a nasty little Roman who is trying to unscrew his head. Right, it's clear. It's up to you!

● Go to **88** to see what is happening.

82

NOW LET'S GET DOWN TO BRASS TACKS...

'Right,' says Cacofonix, looking at you suspiciously. 'Untie me! Let them get on with the fighting, I'm going to give you your second singing lesson. These days the key to success for being an accomplished superstar is the VOICE. Especially if you intend to take part in the Woadstock Festival, in front of hundreds and hundreds of people. It won't be an easy audience, believe me, and in order to make yourself heard, you must have strong vocal chords.' Cacofonix takes from his pocket a small contraption which looks like a sundial.

'Take a good look at this. It's one of my inventions: a vocal-dial. The feather does the job of the indicator. I place the dial in front of your mouth, and it will show what distance your voice reaches.'

You take the deepest possible breath. You mustn't let your teacher down. *To see what distance the dial indicates when you sing, all you have to do is make two throws of the dice, add the numbers together and refer to the middle band of the dial (in Roman numerals). The inner band shows the distance your voice reached and the outer band shows the number of the paragraph you must go to.*

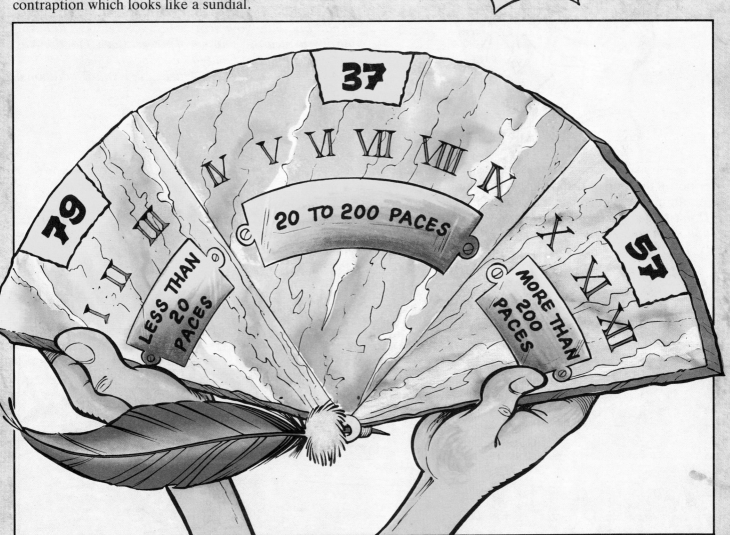

83

After the gushing praise, the accolades, the slaps on the back, everyone sits down at the great banquet table to have breakfast.

'Tell me,' Getafix asks, 'unless I am much mistaken, you still haven't had your ration of magic potion.'
The druid feels in his pockets and pulls out a little leather gourd.

'Guard it closely. With all the ruffians around, you must be careful.'
When you shake the gourd, you are disappointed to find it is nearly empty.

'I'm very sorry,' says Getafix, 'we're a little short of potion at the moment, and this gourd contains only three mouthfuls. You must use it sparingly.'
Don't forget to make a note of these 3 doses of magic potion on your Adventure Slab. Add the gourd as well to the list of objects you are carrying with you. Which ones?

I'll tell you. You can choose a maximum of 4 objects from the following list:

- *a shield, which allows you to add 3 points to your Fighting Fitness*
- *a small pocket knife*
- *two little lozenges for your voice, which will allow you to add 1 point to your score when you're asked to throw the dice to measure your vocal power. Each one counts as one object and can be used only once*
- *a little bottle of scent which gives you 2 additional points of Charm*
- *a lyre string*
- *a small skeleton-key*
- *a whistle*
- *a very elegant red silk scarf*
- *a lucky charm necklace, which adds 2 points to your Skill*
- *a small Roman flute*

If you want to take with you objects that you find on the way, you'll have to swap them, as you're allowed a maximum of only 5.

'Now, my boy, another wild boar leg?' Vitalstatistix suggests after a long moment of collective and culinary concentration.

You politely refuse. For some minutes, it has seemed that there's something not quite right. All around, everyone is looking at you sympathetically. Everyone? No. By Belenos! You've just realised that two people are missing from the banquet table: CACOFONIX and Obelix! What's happened to the bard?

'Wh . . . where is Cacofonix?' you enquire in a faltering voice.

The others look at you and say nothing, obviously embarrassed. It seems no one wants to tell you where your singing teacher is. You fly off the handle. That really is the limit. You realise that the villagers haven't the slightest intention of allowing you to have lessons from Cacofonix. You bang your fist violently on the table, to the amazement of the Gauls.

'What's up? What's the matter?' asks Vitalstatistix.

● In a steady voice you explain the situation. You need at least three singing lessons before the start of the Woadstock Festival. Go to **85**.

● Fearlessly, you set off alone in search of Cacofonix. They must have tied him up somewhere near the village. Go to **62**.

Streptococcus takes you towards a tent in the middle of the fortified camp, whilst another Roman drags Cacofonix towards the stockade. A young girl, who's humming an old Gaulish air, is doing the dishes. She looks up and introduces herself, smiling:

'My name is Serenata. Here you are, I'll wash, you dry.'

A glance outside tells you that the Romans have relaxed their vigilance a little.

● There's not a moment to lose. You make a dash for it across the camp, hoping to escape the legionaries' attention. Go to **51**.

● You decide to enjoy a bit of breathing space and you tell the story of your adventure to the charming Serenata while doing the drying-up. Go to **78**.

The Gauls are all ears and seem to admire your strength of character.

'Shall we see what he's like?' suggests Impedimenta.

'Brilliant idea,' says Asterix. 'Bring him a lyre. Let's hear this famous song.'

● Here is your chance to show what you can do. You wait patiently for them to bring you the lyre. Go to **66**.

● Suspicious, you absolutely refuse to sing before knowing the whereabouts of Cacofonix. Go to **36**.

Alas! The Romans won't allow you a second chance to escape. YOUR ADVENTURE IS OVER.

'Ouch!'

CRACK! BOOM! Getafix has just fallen out of an oak tree a few paces from you. The druid is gathering mistletoe and your loud cry caused him to topple out. He disappears, cursing.

● Go to **72** to have your last lesson from Cacofonix.

CHAPTER III

COLLECTING THE HELMETS

88

The village is deserted. All its inhabitants are busy fighting at the stockade (joyfully and good-humouredly!). The mission Vitalstatistix has entrusted you with is clear: you must bring back the helmets of the five legionaries who are hidden in the village. The only thing you have is a key which you have just picked up and a ladder which is nearby. How are you going to begin? It's up to you to choose.

Turn over the page and you will find a picture of Asterix's small village. A few houses and their doors are marked with a letter. There is also a table which may appear a bit complicated, but don't worry, it's all very simple. Down the column on the left and on the top line of the table certain options are listed like **Asterix's house; Asterix's door; call; ladder,** etc. You have to complete this list as your adventure progresses.

DIRECTIONS FOR USE OF THE TABLE

If you want to call out in front of Asterix's house, take the intersection of the column **call** and the line **Asterix's house,** there you find the number **140** which sends you to the corresponding paragraph. Another example: if you want to go into Obelix's house, take the intersection of the column **enter** and the line corresponding to **Obelix's door**. There you find the number **114** which will tell you what you find in Obelix's house.

To use the key in a door, for example the fishmonger's, all you have to do is read what you find at the intersection of the column **key** and the line **fishmonger's door**.

To use the ladder . . . , well, you work it out for yourself, the principle is the same.

You will see that there are no empty squares in this table. For every action you try, there is a corresponding paragraph. But a bit of thought will prevent you wasting time trying stupid or impossible things. By exploring the possibilities which are now available, you can complete bit by bit the options that are missing on the top line and down the left-hand column.

For example, on your way, you find a lyre. We'll tell you this: this lyre corresponds to the letter V in your table. All you have to do is make a note of **lyre** under that letter and then you can use it, for example in front of the fishmonger's – if the smell doesn't put you off – by tracing the intersection of the column **lyre** with the line **fishmonger**. If someone admires your song you will find out about it in paragraph **128.**

But, since you haven't yet found a lyre, you must forget that example immediately! You can use only those objects that you've already found, in the same way that you can go and do things only in the places that you have already discovered.

In this chapter, you don't need to make a note of the objects you discover on your Adventure Slab.

AIM OF THE GAME

In this apparently deserted village you must find some well-hidden Romans in order to steal their helmets. You need five helmets to earn the lessons you need from Cacofonix. Good luck!

		CALL	ENTER	S	T	U	V	W	X	Y	Z
						KEY				LADDER	
A	ASTERIX'S HOUSE	140	130	99	104	133	108	131	162	100	164
B	ASTERIX'S DOOR	140	112	145	89	153	111	131	103	97	165
C	OBELIX'S HOUSE	113	130	99	104	133	111	131	162	154	166
D	OBELIX'S DOOR	113	114	101	149	153	108	131	103	97	165
E	VITALSTATISTIX'S HOUSE	90	130	99	104	133	95	131	162	125	166
F	VITALSTATISTIX'S DOOR	90	142	101	89	135	111	131	103	97	165
G	CACOFONIX'S HOUSE	136	132	99	104	133	108	131	162	155	166
H	BLACKSMITH'S HOUSE	91	130	99	104	133	108	131	162	156	166
I	BLACKSMITH'S DOOR	91	109	101	137	127	111	131	103	97	165
J	FISHMONGER	92	130	99	104	133	128	150	143	156	166
K	FISHMONGER'S DOOR	92	117	121	137	144	128	94	143	97	165
L		93	118	101	126	146	111	131	123	157	164
M		152	119	145	138	120	108	160	116	158	166
N		152	161	101	126	146	111	131	123	157	166
O		98	105	101	126	146	108	131	123	157	166
P		98	119	101	138	146	108	160	124	158	166
Q		106	106	122	139	147	129	131	115	159	166
R		134	107	102	141	110	96	131	151	163	148

44

89

CRAACK! You have shattered the door with your hammer.
Unfortunately, there's no one inside and nothing at all to report.
Prepare a good excuse, because it could well be that the door's owner
does not appreciate this sort of joke.

90

There's no need to shout yourself hoarse. It seems there's no one there.

91

You can go on yelling till you're blue in the face, there's no one there.

92

There doesn't seem to be anybody there. It's not surprising with that smell!

93

If you climbed up on to that roof just to shout, you would have done better to stay down below.

94

Thanks to the clothes-peg, you can at last go into the fishmonger's.
There's nothing left except one large fish which you take with you. *This particularly odorous*
fish *corresponds to the letter X along the top row of your table. Make good use of it.*

95

The walls of this house have no ears.

96

Your lyre does not frighten the Bellicus brothers. Try something else. It's very, very urgent.

97

Never place a ladder against a door! Do we have to draw a picture?

TO FULFIL YOUR MISSION

YOU HAVE A KEY AND A LADDER. BUT FACED WITH ROMAN...

98

You shout as loud as you can and suddenly a small Roman legionary
jumps out from behind the chimney breast, holding his ears.
'Stop shouting like that! I've got a terrible pain in my ears,' he protests. 'Here's my helmet,
you've won. Don't try and torture me. I shan't tell you where my friends are,
nor the password! I can resist nearly all forms of pressure!'
This particularly timid legionary is called **Timorus:**
he corresponds to the letter Q on the left-hand column of the table. If you still don't have the four
other helmets, you ought to try to exert some pressure on Timorus by using the objects
in your possession. Don't hesitate to use them. You can find other means as well to make him speak.
Taking hold of his helmet, you notice, engraved inside, the number XXXIV.
Probably a lucky number. Even so, make a note of it, it might come in handy. *If you have
already found the four other helmets, you will have carefully made a note of their respective numbers.
By adding the five numbers together, you will find the number of the paragraph you must go to.*

99

The walls of this house have no ears. Try something else.

100

Here you are on the roof.
The **roof** *of this house corresponds to the letter L in the left-hand column.*
A **menhir** is placed precariously there, just above the porch. During the fight, Obelix didn't know his own
strength, as usual.
The precarious **menhir** *corresponds to the letter Z in the top row. Put it to good use!*
There is a **chimney** *on this roof, which corresponds to the letter M in the left-hand column.*
Write the name of the owner of this house on your grid as a reference.

101

No reply.

102

'That's him, the little Gaul who knows our password,' exclaims one of the Bellicus brothers.
'Catch him boys. We'll smash him to pulp!'
It might have been better not to attract their attention. If you don't want any trouble,
use another means available from your table. It's very, very urgent.

103

You do realise, don't you, that a door is an inanimate object?

104

The walls of this house are solid. Why don't you try with your head, to see. . . .

105

What do you mean exactly by 'entering Vitalstatistix's roof'? Try something else.

106

Timorus doesn't like that one little bit. Find something else.

107

Give up trying to get into the house of the Bellicus brothers, it could cost you dear. Look for another means by using your table and the objects available . . . but do it quickly!

108

The sound of this instrument is much too weak and has no effect.

109

The door is locked. It's useless to go on trying.

110

Your key doesn't frighten the Bellicus brothers. Find another method – and fast!

111

Your music doesn't interest anyone in the neighbourhood.

112

The door of this house is locked. Don't waste any more time trying the impossible.

113

No one answers your calls.

114

This door is locked. Its owner must be afraid of menhir burglars.

115

Timorus does not have a particularly well-developed sense of smell. . . .

116

Your secret weapon falls down the chimney with immediate effect.
The Bellicus brothers cough, spit, shout out and finally stagger from the house with
tears streaming down their faces. There they are, all four of them, gathered in the porch.
This could be the ideal moment to attack them, but what with?
The Bellicus brothers, in this very favourable position for you, correspond to the letter R in the left-hand column.
If you want to put pressure on them don't stint yourself.
It is in fact very, very urgent. . . .

117

The door is open. The smell is so atrocious that even burglars run away. The fishmonger is right.
It is impossible for you to step inside without making yourself ill.
Is there a knack to it?

118

What do you mean exactly by 'entering the roof' of this house? Have a little think . . .

119

What do you think you're up to? That's your bad luck! Since Gaulish chimneys are narrow, you remain stuck
there until someone comes to help you. You'll never hear the end of it!

120

If you go on acting the goat, the key will fall down the chimney and that will be a fat lot of good . . .

121

No one in the fishmonger's answers the password . . . they're as dumb as oysters!

122

'Stop shouting the password in my ear!' Timorus complains.
'You'd be better employed looking for the Bellicus brothers.'
There's something in what Timorus says . . .

123

What effect are you hoping to produce like that?

124

If you continue to monkey about, your fish will fall down the chimney . . .

125

You climb on to the roof and your sensitive hearing catches a slight noise . . . However, there's nothing
to be seen. Might it be the effect of fear?
*The **roof** of this house corresponds to the letter O in the left-hand column.*
*There is a **chimney** on this roof which corresponds to the letter P in the left-hand column.*
Write the name of the owner on the roof and the chimney on your grid as a reference.

126

When you have made a hole in the roof, the rain will come through. And then what?

127

CLICK! CLACK!
The door opens like a charm. Inside the house, you discover some anvils,
a large hammer and, what a surprise, a . . . clothes-peg which no doubt allows the owner of this house
to put up with the smells from the nearby fishmonger's.
*On your table, the **hammer** corresponds to the letter T in the top row.*
*The **clothes-peg** corresponds to the letter W.*
Now you can use these two objects in any way you like. Don't try and remove the anvils,
that would be a weighty problem!

128

Music hath no charms to soothe a savage smell . . .

129

Since your instrument is not very powerful, you have the great idea of pinning Timorus against the chimney and playing a tune directly into his ear. He crumbles in tears and drops his helmet. 'Stop it! Stop it! You have found the only means of making me talk! I confess everything. There are four other legionaries hidden in one of the village houses: the four Bellicus brothers! But watch out, they are fierce fighters and it won't be easy to dislodge them. They've got just one weakness: a hypersensitive sense of smell. If you want the password, I'll give it to you as a bonus. It is "Gather thistles, expect prickles!"'
The password which Timorus has just revealed corresponds to the letter S (top row of the table). You can shout it as often as you like. You also noticed that inside the helmet that Timorus had just dropped, there was a number: XXXIV. This might come in useful. Make a note of it.
As for the Bellicus brothers, it is time to deal with them!

130

It would be easier to go through the door!

131

The clothes-peg is not much use here. Have a little think before trying any old thing . . . .

132

It's impossible to get into this house. Who has dared take the ladder?
If you knew where it was, you could use it . . .

133

You don't use a key in a wall. Why not try the door?

134

'What is it?' enquires the eldest Bellicus brother.
'Catch him, boys, we'll give him a lesson!'
You can get out of this if you use your brain . . . and the means available in your table for fighting, but be quick . . .

135

The key remains stuck in the door. But is it the right door?
Phew! You've managed to get the key out.

136

No one answers your calls.

137

Why struggle with an unlocked door?

138

Your hammer has fallen down the chimney. If you want to go on banging anywhere,
you will have to use your head. . . .

139

Bashing the head of a defeated legionary without a his helmet isn't exactly humane. A black mark against you.

140

No one answers your calls.

141

It's impossible to knock out all the Bellicus brothers with one single hammer blow. They are not too
kindly disposed towards you for having tried. It's in your own interest to try something else, and fast!

142

The door is locked. It's a simple precautionary measure, given the uncertain times
and the endless fighting . . .

143

You're taking the fish back to the fishmonger's? You're within your rights. But you won't be
able to use it again. So, I should have a good think first.

144

Why break down an open door?

145

The reaction was not slow in coming.
'Who's there?' whispers a voice, inside the house.
At least now, you know where the Bellicus brothers are.
Now it's up to you to dislodge them and get hold of their helmets!

146

There's no keyhole on this roof . . .

147

Your key does not frighten Timorus.

148

Well done! The menhir is swaying. You push a little more and suddenly it falls on the Bellicus brothers
and knocks them out. All you have to do now is get down from the roof and pick up
their helmets (which are as flat as pancakes after what has fallen on them!).
You can read a number, probably a lucky charm, in each of them.
Here they are: XXX, XXV, LX, XVIII.
*If you have already found one helmet with a number in, all you have to do is add up the
five numbers and go to the corresponding paragraph.*
But if you haven't got this fifth helmet, you must look for a little legionary
who is hiding in the village.
Don't be afraid, he is quite harmless!

149

The door resists even your strongest pushes. But with Obelix they need to have solid door-frames as well!

150

Ah! What a pleasure it is to be able to walk near the fishmongers without having to put up with particularly
disagreeable smells. You understand immediately the usefulness of the blacksmith's invention!

151

Justforkix! You can't use your fish any more because you have just dropped it down
Asterix's chimney!

152

No one answers your calls.

153

The door refuses to open. Perhaps it's not the right door?
Unless of course it isn't the right key . . .

154

You climb on to the roof. There's no one there and nothing to report.
*The **roof** of this house corresponds to the letter N in your table.*
Write it on your grid as well as the owner's name.

155

This house is empty, but you find a magnificent lyre which you can use if you wish.
*This **lyre** corresponds to the letter V in the table.*

156

It's impossible to climb on to the roof of this house. There's no room for the ladder.

157

What are you going to do with a ladder on a roof?

158

The ladder won't go down the chimney.

159

Your ladder does not impress Timorus.

NOTHING EQUALS THE HAMMER...

NOW, LADDIE, THE THING IS TO STRIKE WHILE THE IRON IS...

BANG. BANG.

BIFF!

WHEN IT'S USED

...HOT...

SPLATCH!

...WITH SKILL AND DYNAMISM...

AND HERE'S A STRIKING EXAMPLE OF ACTING IN THE HEAT OF THE MOMENT.

!

{160}

If you go on playing the fool, your clothes-peg will fall down the chimney. . . .

{161}

What exactly do you mean by 'entering the roof' of this house? Try something else.

{162}

No reaction.

{163}

Your ladder does not impress the Bellicus brothers. Try something else, and be quick.

{164}

The menhir is already on the house.

{165}

It won't go through the door. You can stop trying.

{166}

You can't possibly carry the menhir as far as that.

{167}

You come across Vitalstatistix in front of the village gate, still struggling with the Romans
(who are just about to lose the fight, but the Gauls like to prolong the pleasure!).
'You've brought the five helmets!' exclaims Vitalstatistix. 'Well done my boy!
How many lessons do you still need to have?'

• You still haven't yet had a lesson with Cacofonix. Go to **168**.

• You have had your first lesson with Cacofonix, so you are able to decipher this small score and find the number of the paragraph where you will receive your second lesson.

• You have already had your first and second lessons from Cacofonix and so you are able to decipher this little score and find the number of the paragraph where you are expected for your third lesson.

168

'Many congratulations!' exclaims Cacofonix, putting his hand on your shoulder.
While the others go on fighting, you both move away from the battlefield.
'I am going to give you your first singing lesson. First of all, you must learn how to read music.'
In the distance, you hear the din of battle, but, quite calmly, Cacofonix engraves the five parallel lines of a musical stave on a strip of bark.

'Now then,' he continues, 'the lowest note is called Doh. Above is Ray. As you go up, you have Me, Fah, Soh, Lah, Te, then, once again, Doh, Ray, and so on . . . . Do you understand?'
You nod your head.
'Very good,' says Cacofonix. 'Did you know that in olden times musicians sometimes sent coded messages in the form of a little five note tune?
Here is the system. You never know, it might come in useful.
Doh is worth 1, Ray = 2, Me = 3, Fah = 4, Soh = 5, Lah = 6, Te = 7.
To arrive at the number of the message, you have to multiply the first four note-figures together, and add the fifth to the total obtained.

• *That's a very interesting piece of information isn't it? Cacofonix whistles a little five note melody.*
Can you decode it and find the number of the paragraph you must go to now?

CHAPTER IV

AT POPMUSIX'S VILLA

169

The house of the famous singer, Popmusix, is situated near the beach at Woadstock where the festival is held. It's a Gallo-Roman style villa, unpretentious but in good taste. Crossing the little bridge, you notice a small group of people who are waiting for the man they call the King of Gaulish Rock. Your first objective is to get Popmusix to see you. After that, you will have to find out how to get on to the stage at Woadstock for your triumphal debut.

Take care: this chapter contains a well-kept secret. It's up to you to learn it to finish this adventure. Naturally, you will learn more once you have met Popmusix and know the purpose of this final puzzle. In order to solve it, you will have to go back to places you have already visited. In some paragraphs, certain options are available only if you know the answer to this puzzle. So don't worry about those options. You might also be lucky enough to find the solution to this enigma during your first visit!

Each number written on the picture (following page) corresponds to a group of people or to a particular location and tells you which paragraph you must go to. You can travel about quite freely.

170

A few young people dressed in a way-out fashion greet you, smiling sarcastically. Your clothes embarrass you a little, because you realise how shabby you look compared to these elegant young people. And you always thought you were up with the latest Lutetia fashion!

'Hey! The Hix*!' shouts one of the young people. 'What are you doing here?'

'You're not going to tell us that you hope to meet Popmusix dressed like that?'

You are even more embarrassed. Fortunately, a girl in the group intervenes:

'Leave him alone, he's not as bad as all that. What d'you do then, kid? D'you milk the cows or look after the pigs?'

Everyone bursts out laughing.

● It's no use hanging around here. You decide to go elsewhere. *Consult the picture.*

● Feeling cross, you announce you're a singer and that you'll prove it. Go to **195**.

*Hick.

171

'Hey, look! I know him!'

It's the girl Sonatina whom you met before. She looks admiringly at your hair.

'Yes, he's not bad,' says the other girl.

'Oh! I would give absolutely anything to have a lock of his hair . . .'

● Have you heard about women who cast spells on people. A lock of hair is exactly what they use for their wicked acts. If you have, you decide you've heard enough and run off. . . . *Consult the picture.*

● You don't think Sonatina is the sort to cast spells. You would even be flattered to give her a lock of your hair. Go to **190**.

172

A window in Popmusix's house opens. Everyone rushes forward:

'Popmusix! Hurray for Popmusix!'

The star just manages a little wave and asks in a loud voice:

'Who uttered that magnificent howl?'

Silence. You put your hand up and go forward.

'You?' asks Popmusix. 'I should like to speak to you.'

Popmusix turns to his guards:

'Let him in.'

● If it's the first time you've met Popmusix, go to **176**.

● If, during your adventure, you've already met Popmusix, go to **206**.

173

Two rather unfriendly guards, seeing you come forward, question you:

'Hold it there, kid! What d'you want?'

• You can show them a letter of introduction (*it must be listed on your Adventure Slab*). Go to **176**.
• You have already met Popmusix, so the guards recognise you and let you in. Go to **206**.
• You've no letter and haven't met the singer before. Go to **200**.

174

Were you wondering what the badge is for? Nothing.
• You could, of course, swap it by going back to **181**.
• If you want to keep it, go wherever you like. *Consult the picture.*

175

The man, who keeps himself hidden in the shadows of Popmusix's house, whispers to you conspiratorially:

'Have you got any money?'

'A little,' you reply, too quickly.

'I can get you what you're looking for,' says the man. Is he telling the truth? Can he really sell you an original tune cheaply? That's what you're going to find out.

'Let's get away from here,' he adds. 'We'll settle this round the back.' You hear someone whistling in the distance, from the direction this mysterious character is pointing to.

• You don't want to take any risks and so you decide to go elsewhere. *Consult the picture.*
• The man's plan seems interesting and you are curious to know where this melodious whistling is coming from. Go to **182**.

176

Popmusix asks you to come in. You explain that you are Cacofonix's pupil and that you would like to take part in the Woadstock Festival.

'Very well, my boy. Cacofonix is a very great bard. They'll certainly let you sing in the afternoon.'

Isn't that wonderful? Everything suddenly seems so easy! All at once, however, Popmusix seems rather worried.

'Tell me, I suppose you've got a modern instrument?'

'A modern instrument? What do you mean by that?' you ask, puzzled.

'I mean a Harpelectrix. It's a lyre made by the stringed-instrument maker Harpelectrix, whose power allows it to reach the last rows of the audience in the largest festivals. That's something you need to know!'

'Listen. A Roman merchant, crazy about music, came this way recently. He wanted to swap a Harpelectrix for an original song. I think he's camping near here waiting for the festival to open.'

Popmusix tells you how to find this merchant and gives you a letter of recommendation to get on the stage at the festival.

• You're going to get the merchant to swap his Harp-electrix? But what with? An original song, but what song? . . . And where can you find one? . . . Go to **214**, to find the answers to these serious questions.

 177

The guards take your sestertii and usher you in to Pop-musix.
• Go to **176**

178

Do you still believe in those silly things, at your age? The stone falls down . . . right on your head!
• You can still swap it (the stone, not your head) by going back to **181**.
• If you prefer to keep it, go wherever you like. *Consult the picture*.

179

What a crowd! This character – *invisible in the picture* – was hiding behind the right-hand corner of Popmusix's house. *Now, it's in your interest to write the number 201*

precisely at that spot on your picture. In this way, you will be able to find this discreet character again, even if his proposition doesn't interest you for the moment . . .
• You wish to know more. Go to **201**.
• You prefer to ignore this shady character and go where you like. *Consult the picture*.

180

'Fifty sestertii?' says one of them. 'If you want us to let you in, you will need at least twice as much.'
You go off, cursing your bad luck. Suddenly, a character invisible up to that point emerges from behind the corner of Popmusix's house. There really are a lot of people about! *This character was not shown in the picture because he was hidden from view, behind the right-hand corner of Popmusix's house. Now, it is in your interest to write the number 201 at this spot on your picture. In this way you can keep track of this shady character. You never know!*

• You wish to know more. Go to **201**.
• You prefer to pay no attention to this strange person and you go off on another tack. *Consult the picture*.

181

Here are the objects that Sonatina gives you. You may choose one and *go to the corresponding paragraph. Don't forget to make a note on your Slab of every object you take with you.*

- A hair-brush with wild boar bristles. Go to **204**.
- A badge with Popmusix's picture on it. Go to **174**.
- A small piece of slate. Go to **188**.
- A little grey-coloured stone. Go to **185**.
- A pocket mirror. Go to **199**.
- A very old roll of papyrus. Go to **196**.

182

Behind the house, you're just in time to catch sight of a silhouette jumping from one of the windows and disappearing into a thicket, whistling. Did you pay any attention to the tune he was whistling? It's a pity you didn't notice it. Sharper reflexes would not come amiss. *Mark the thicket into which the man disappeared with a little X on the picture, and you can now add a number, 208, to enable you to go back there whenever you want.*

- This strange character, who has just come out of Popmusix's house, interests you. You rush towards the thicket, just behind the house at **208**.
- You prefer to make a deal with the other man. Go to **186**.

183

You cross the little bridge and go towards a house whose shutters are all closed. There doesn't appear to be anyone there. . . KNOCK KNOCK! You knock at the door but there's no reply. Could there be a secret code?
- If you know the code, you'll know what to do. . . .
- If not, go to **205**.

184

'And what are you doing here?' you ask politely.
'I'm waiting for my friend, as always. I think she would like you a lot. She would love your hair! Would you like to wait with me? You never know with Sonatina how long you'll have to wait. She's never on time whenever we arrange to meet. . .'

- That's hard luck on Sonatina, but you have better things to do than to wait for a girl who would love your hair. *Consult the picture.*
- You decide to wait for Sonatina, to see if she really does like your hair. Go to **171**.

185

This little grey-coloured stone is very pretty but not particularly useful at the moment!
- You can swap it by going back to **181**.
- If you would rather keep it, go wherever you like. *Consult the picture.*
- What if this were a magic stone? Perhaps all you have to do is throw it in the air for it to fall on some significant spot. For that, go to **178**.

186

'We won't be disturbed here,' the man says, 'show me what you've got.'
You empty your pockets in front of the stranger so that he can decide on a price. Quick as a flash he grabs your sestertii and looks at you, slyly.
'That's the sort of deal I like!'
Too late. This man is nothing but a common scoundrel. Are you prepared to prevent him running off with your fortune? Use your fists, it's very good for your health. *The thief's Fighting Fitness score is 23.*
- If you win, go to **193**.
- If you lose, go to **189**.

187

You show the guards the extent of your fortune.
- You possess fifty sestertii. Go to **180**.
- You possess one hundred sestertii. Go to **177**.
- You don't speak about money to strangers. You move away and go wherever you like. *Consult the picture.*

188

What are you going to do with this piece of slate? Night is falling and you can't see a thing. Besides, Sonatina and her friend are ready to leave . . .

- If you're quick about it, you can still swap your piece of slate by going back to **181**.
- If you want to examine the slate in the light, go up to the house, at **212**.
- Alternatively, you can take the slate with you and go wherever you like. *Consult the picture.*

189

You can cross out this scoundrel's address on your picture, but unfortunately he has just had a profitable day at your expense. If he reappears, pretend you're not there. *You can also cross out everything you had in your pocket as you've nothing left. And cross out the guards on your picture.* Without any money you can't bribe them.
- *Consult the picture.*

190

'Just a minute, I should have a pair of scissors,' says Sonatina, smiling.
She takes from her bag several small objects among which is a pair of scissors and she uses them to cut off a lock of your hair.
'Thank you. I really love that colour of hair. I swear I'll take precious care of it. Here . . . in exchange you can help yourself to one of these objects, if you wish.'
- Night is falling, you must get on. Go where you like on the picture.
- If one of Sonatina's objects interests you, go to **181**.

191

You have knocked eight times and you hear footsteps on the other side of the door. To your great surprise, you see Myopia, one of your Aunt Impedimenta's friends!

'Here's a surprise! Justforkix. How nice of you to come and visit me! What brings you here?'

'Er . . . er . . .' you stammer, as she ushers you into her house.

After the inevitable nettle soup, you tell Myopia, who is a little deaf, the reason for your visit.

'I'm sure Popmusix, my neighbour, will certainly help you. Would you like to meet him? He loves my nettle soup and he's always pleased to see me.'

- If you haven't met Popmusix yet, that is certainly what you want more than anything else. So you go along with the suggestion and Myopia, hobbling along, takes you to his house. Go to **176**.
- Even if you have already met Popmusix, you can pay him another visit, in which case Myopia takes you to his house at **206**.
- If, for any reason, you think that Popmusix can't help you in your search, don't count on Myopia to sing you something original. She is as deaf as a post. Thank her and say goodbye and go wherever you like. *Consult the picture.*

192

Sitting on a bench, four Gauls are playing dice.

'If you want to get in to see Popmusix,' says one of them, 'you have to pay the guards a hundred sestertii.'

'Well, my lad, d'you want to join the game?' enquires another Gaul.

- If you have some money and you want to join the game, go to **207**.
- If you haven't any money, or if you don't want to join the game, you have lost nothing. *Consult the picture.*

193

Well done! You've beaten him. You pull his ears really hard and, not being used to this sort of treatment, the man begins to groan with pain:

'Stop it! Stop it! You're hurting. All right, I'll give you back your money.'

He gives you back your purse and runs back into the bushes, dropping a 50 sestertii coin. As you've no desire to run after him to give it back, you now have an extra 50 sestertii!

Make a note of them on your Adventure Slab.

- Consult the picture.

194

A pretty young girl is sitting in the shade of a tree. She looks at you intently as you approach her. What she is in fact doing is judging your charm. It is extremely difficult to charm this young girl. You must really shine if you want to interest her. *In fact, if you don't pass this test of Charm, (difficulty 20, which seems impossible and yet . . .) she won't even speak to you.*

- If you pass, go to **211**.
- If you fail, she turns away and refuses to speak to you. Obviously there's something wrong with your appearance. What on earth could it be? *Consult the picture.*

63

195

SOCK IT TO US!

Perhaps it's a bit risky singing like that, so ear-piercingly, in front of strangers. But the important thing is to have a voice which carries, especially as one of the young people has just taken from his pocket a small contraption, the same as the one Cacofonix has. In technical terms the instrument is called a vocal-dial but it is known more commonly as a 'screechometer'. You already know how to use this 'dial' – at least we hope you do. If not, it means you haven't taken in Cacofonix's second lesson.

● If you are weak or feeble, you can't go on. *Consult the picture.*

LALA

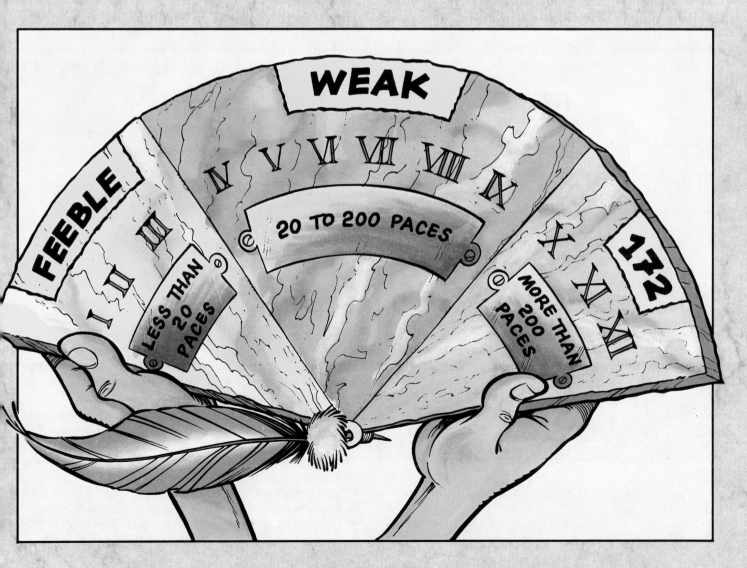

WEAK

V VI VII VIII IX

20 TO 200 PACES

FEEBLE

I II III

LESS THAN 20 PACES

X XI XII

MORE THAN 200 PACES

172

196

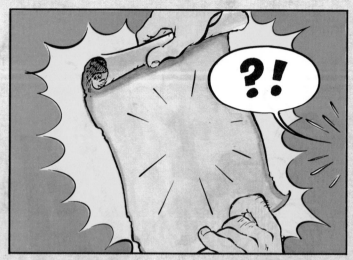

You unroll the papyrus. Unfortunately, it's completely empty.

● You can swap it by going back to **181**.
● If you prefer to keep it, go wherever you like. *Consult the picture*.
● You can also try dipping it in water to see if it contains a message written in invisible ink. Go to **198**.

197

Well done! You've managed to lean over the water without dropping anything. It's just that a light breeze has ruffled the surface, stopping you from seeing your reflection. That's all.

● You can wait until the wind dies down, if you so wish. Go to **213**.
● You have wasted enough time here. Go wherever you like. *Consult the picture*.

198

What a strange idea! The papyrus crumbles in your hands.

● You can still swap the pieces, if you don't mind Sonatina thinking you're an idiot, by going back to **181**.
● You can go wherever you like. *Consult the picture*.

199

You look at yourself in the mirror. Not bad, not bad at all, kid! But what's new?

● You can swap the mirror by going back to **181**.
● If you prefer to keep it, go wherever you like. *Consult the picture*.

200

One of the guards is nonchalantly playing with a gold coin. From that you deduce that with a little bribe they may perhaps let you in.

'Now my lad, you wouldn't happen to have any money on you, by any chance?' asks the other guard.

● If you have some money on you, go to **187**.
● If you are completely out of pocket, go somewhere else. *Consult the picture*.

201

The man, who still remains hidden in the shadow of Popmusix's house, greets you with a smile and whispers conspiratorially:

'I can arrange a meeting with the singer. Come over here. Let's get out of the way, we can settle this affair round the back.'

You hear someone whistling in the distance, from the direction the man points to.

● You prefer not to take any risks and continue on your way to wherever you like. *Consult the picture*.
● His proposition interests you. You follow it up at **182**. In this way, you'll learn where the whistling comes from.

202

The footprints disappear into a bush. You go all round it and, by Toutatis! three Roman deserters jump out on you. There's not a moment to lose, you must fight. *Their total Fighting Fitness score is 32.*
• If you lose, go to **215**, haunted by that melodious tune.
• You have won. Go wherever you like, but don't come back to this bush. *Consult the picture.*

203

All right, you threw a few pebbles but you're not there to waste time.
• *Consult the picture* (and try to do something more interesting).

204

You're brushing your hair? So what?
• Sonatina will be quite willing to swap this brush if you go back to **181**.
• You can go wherever you like. *Consult the picture.*

205

I'm very sorry, but if you're standing in front of this door without knowing how to get it opened, you must have cheated somewhere.
• Go wherever you like. *Consult the picture.*

206

'Well, well, my boy! So you've come back? To what do we owe this second visit?'

You explain to Popmusix that you're looking for an original song. But Popmusix doesn't seem to appreciate hearing this and quickly shows you to the door, frowning.
   'There have been a lot of thieves in these parts lately.' Speaking to his guards he adds:
   'You lot! Don't let anybody else in. Do you understand?'
   'OK, chief!'
Numbed by a well-aimed kick, you are trying to get up when you hear a voice whispering in your ear:
   'Come this way, I've got what you need . . .'
• Go to **175**.

207

The heftiest Gaul settles down opposite you. Don't worry, it is not a complicated game.
Here are the rules of the game:
– Each throw is worth 10 sestertii, so you must take away 10 sestertii from your pile each time your opponent scores more than you, and add 10 sestertii to it each time you win.
– If you both score the same number of points, you leave the money on the table and add another 10 sestertii (so the next throw is worth 20 sestertii).
– There's no point in playing with money you don't possess, because it doesn't look as if the Gauls are playing for fun.
– The first throw is for the Gaul, the second for you.
– You may stop playing whenever you wish, whether you're winning or losing and you can pass the 100 sestertii limit if you feel your luck's in.
– The Gauls have 300 sestertii. So in this game, the maximum you can win is what you started with, plus their 300 sestertii.

● If you have won 100 sestertii or more, you can go to the guards at **177**, where at last you will be able to meet Popmusix.
● If you have lost or stopped playing without having won, try something else. Everything is possible. *Consult the picture.*

208

There's no one in sight. The footprints, however, disappear in the direction of the forest.
● You decide to follow these footprints. Go to **202**.
● Oh dear! It's too dangerous to venture into the forest, so you return to the house. *Consult the picture.*

209

Perhaps you will do better next time.
● *Consult the picture.*

210

A small path leads down to the river. At the water's edge, you can:
● Pick up a pebble and play ducks and drakes. Go to **203**.
● Look into the water. It seems that poets do that all the time. But take care leaning over the water, something might slip out of your pocket and you won't be able to get it back. Go to **197**.

211

'Hello! Haven't we met somewhere before?'
Before you have time to reply, she goes on:
'What are you doing round here?'
You explain the situation.
'Why not try over there first? It's the house of one of Popmusix's girlfriends.
The girl points to a little house, on the other side of the river, that you hadn't noticed before. Now you can go there if you wish. *Yes, the house is quite visible in the picture, you can see its roof on the extreme left among the trees. You can write down its address – 183 – on your picture in order to find it easily later on.*
● You say goodbye to the girl and rush to **183**.
● You continue your conversation with the girl. Go to **184**.

212

By Belenos! Turning your piece of slate towards the light, you notice a small musical stave drawn on it.
● If you wish to read, and especially decipher, this stave, go back to **76**.

213

The wind has dropped. The silence is broken by a noise . . . KNOCK, KNOCK, KNOCK, KNOCK, KNOCK, KNOCK, KNOCK, KNOCK, like someone knocking at a door. But where on earth can it be coming from? That's strange, those eight knocks sound like a signal. Why not try out this signal on a door other than Popmusix's. *All you have to do is add the number 8 to the number of the paragraph where you are at that moment and you will find the number of the paragraph that you are looking for. Don't forget this detail!* And since the wind has dropped, you can at last take your time looking at your reflection in the river. It is then you notice that you have a huge black stain on your cheek. No one has told you about it! You wash your face quickly, wondering when you acquired this dirty mark. After your little wash you look much more attractive. *You may add 100 points to your attraction quotient during this chapter, and in this way it will come back to its normal level. These 100 points will allow you to take an apparently impossible test!*

● Now you may go where you like. *Consult the picture.*

214

You see the large frame of Oesofagus standing at the spot that Popmusix pointed to, in front of the entrance to the Woadstock Festival, where a noisy, motley throng is already gathering. They are eagerly anticipating three days of music and festivity. You introduce yourself to Oesofagus, a wine merchant, who loves songs. But his main aim in life is to register an original song with the Society of Bard Composers, whose tent you can see near the festival entrance. When a singer registers a new song, he receives a sort of diploma, and for years now Oesofagus has been dreaming of framing one of these and hanging it on the wall at home, freed from the task of constantly looking for an original melody.

'Sit down, my boy,' says the music-loving merchant. 'So you would like to buy my Harpelectrix?' He takes from his bag a beautifully-made instrument.

'Look at this . . . or, rather, listen . . . ' With his thumb the merchant delicately touches one string of the lyre. The sound is so loud that several people turn round to look.

'Do you hear? The man who makes these lyres is a real magician. He sells only two of them every year.' Open-mouthed in amazement, you can't take your eyes off the instrument!

'You see,' says Oesofagus, 'this wonderful instrument costs hundreds of sestertii, but I have a proposition that might interest you. I've got many more sestertii than I shall ever need. If you can find me an original tune, I'll give you this Harpelectrix in exchange. What do you say?'

Not yet! Although you are near the last page, your adventure is not yet over. The only way to get on the stage is to find a tune for this merchant. The original tune he is asking for contains a message in the code that Cacofonix explained to you in his first lesson. Do you remember? If not, you're as dead as a dodo. You'll have to start again. Now you'll have to go back to Popmusix's villa. You may have found the means of meeting Popmusix quite quickly the first time you went there, but now you will have to explore the picture using your head and showing more persistence.

● Go to **169**.

• If you happened to find the tune on your first visit to Popmusix, you can obviously calculate the number of the relevant paragraph and make your way there.

• If you can't remember the code used by the bards, or if you didn't make a note of it on your Slab, bad luck! Go to **215**.

• Otherwise, you're on your way back to Popmusix's villa. Good luck! Nothing has changed since your last visit. *The tune may possibly be revealed as much in the text as in the pictures of the paragraphs where you go.* Finally, one last piece of advice: think carefully about Cacofonix's three lessons. They contain more than one precious clue so it's in your interest to remind yourself of them. You go to **169**, and good luck!

215

You guessed it. YOUR ADVENTURE IS OVER!

216

Unforgettable! Hundreds and hundreds of people are there in the audience: they are waiting for the singers and it would never occur to them to tie the performers to a tree! That's what you call artistic sensitivity. And now you're being propelled towards the stage. You don't even have time to feel stage fright. No sooner have you touched the strings of your Harpelectrix than the sound of the instrument reaches the last rows, rousing the crowd to a frenzy. In the audience, several of your friends are wide-eyed in astonishment when they recognise you and, intoxicated by your own ability, you sing at the top of your voice, as in a dream, without making a mistake. Wonderful! Sensational! Inimitable! An uproarious ovation greets your last chord. Hooray! Bravo! You have become a superstar! And in the village that evening, there will be such a feast that even Cacofonix, your singing-teacher, will take part in the banquet!

END

of the adventure

PRINTED IN BELGIUM BY
proost
INTERNATIONAL BOOK PRODUCTION